C000138879

BEST

RUN FASTER

RUNNER'S WORLD® BEST

RUN FASTER

Edited by Adam Bean,
Runner's World® Magazine

RODALE

This edition first published in 2006 by
Rodale International Ltd
7–10 Chandos Street
London
W1G 9AD
www.rodalebooks.co.uk

© 2006 Rodale, Inc.

Runner's World Best® is a registered trademark of Rodale Inc.

Text written by Cree Hale Krull.

Interior Photographs: Brand X Pictures: 94; Comstock: 19, 67, 72; Corbis: 58; Digital Vision: 15, 28, 31, 36, 52, 57, 79; Eyewire: 60; Image Source: 38, 49; © 2006 JupiterImages Corporation: 25; LLC, FogStock: 17, 77, 91; MedioImages: 22; Michael Mazzeo: 40, 41, 42, 43, 44, 45; Photodisk: 18, 35, 74, 84; photolibrary. com pty. ltd: 70; Pixtal: 86; Rodale Photo Library: 6, 9, 10, 13, 26, 29, 32, 46, 47, 50, 55, 63, 64, 66, 69, 82, 92; Thinkstock: 80, 88
Cover Photograph: Michael Medby

All rights reserved. No part of this publication may be reproduced or transmitted in any form or by any means, electronic or mechanical, including photocopying, recording or any other information storage and retrieval system, without the written permission of the publisher.

A CIP record for this book is available from the British Library

Printed and bound in the UK by CPI Bath using acid-free paper from sustainable sources.

1 3 5 7 9 8 6 4 2

ISBN-10: 1-4050-8804-4
ISBN-13: 978-1-4050-8804-6

This paperback edition distributed to the book trade by Pan Macmillan Ltd

Notice

The information in this book is meant to supplement, not replace, proper exercise training. All forms of exercise pose some inherent risks. The editors and publisher advise readers to take full responsibility for their safety and know their limits. Before practising the running programmes and exercises in this book, be sure that your equipment is well maintained, and do not take risks beyond your level of experience, aptitude, training and fitness.

The exercise and dietary programmes in this book are not intended as a substitute for any exercise routine or dietary regime that may have been prescribed by your doctor. As with all exercise and dietary programmes, you should get your doctor's approval before beginning.

Visit us on the Web at *www.runnersworld.co.uk*

Also available: *Runner's World Best: Run Faster.*

Produced by:
Hydra Packaging
129 Main Street, Suite C
Irvington, NY 10533
USA
www.hylaspublishing.com

We inspire and enable people to improve their lives and the world around them

CONTENTS

Challenge your body and mind by running further and faster.

Introduction

If you're reading this book, you probably consider yourself an intermediate-level runner. Even if you *don't* consider yourself an intermediate, this book can help you get there. For more information, see *Is this Book Right for Me?* opposite). Like the unlabelled space between points A and B, 'intermediate' implies a certain transition, rather than a resting place. Consider the analogous terms used in the field of medicine: one begins as a medical student, graduates to become a junior doctor and only becomes fully qualified after gaining considerable knowledge and experience. As a runner who has left behind the beginner stages only to realize how much more there is to know, stop and take pride in where you are now. This book will help you to graduate to the next level in your running life.

In any discipline, achievement rests on a solid grasp of the fundamentals; Part I of this book, *Back to Basics*, reinforces those basic elements that support your running efforts. After a discussion about reaching your goals, you'll then learn about cycle training – an innovative workout plan that ensures you get the training you need, with enough rest included so you won't overtrain. Nutrition and hydration strategies to energize your running take centre stage next, and we conclude the section with a discussion of running surfaces – tarmac, grass and dirt – and how important it is to run on a variety of surfaces.

Part II, *Speed Work Essentials*, introduces new concepts, workouts and gives plenty of advice to help you run faster, whether or not you want to race. Fartleks, hills, tempo runs, intervals – you may have heard the terms and perhaps even have some experience with

IS THIS BOOK RIGHT FOR ME?

When it comes to running, one size doesn't fit all. This is the book for you if:

- You have completed the running plans in the first book of this series, *Runner's World Best: Getting Started.*
- You have been running for at least 3 months, 3 to 5 days each week, for at least 30 minutes per day.
- You have experienced no running-related injuries in the last 3 months.
- You are interested in racing and improving your race times.

If you're just beginning your running journey, you may want to take a step back and read *Runner's World Best: Getting Started,* which features two easy-to-follow running plans that will get you off the sofa and onto the road, enjoying running without injury. If you're already racing successfully, congratulate yourself!

some of these workouts; already in this section you'll expand your knowledge significantly about the distinct benefits and challenges of each type of speed work. You'll also learn about heart-rate monitors and the integral role they can play in focusing your level of aerobic effort for maximum training benefits.

What you do before and after you run can have an enormous impact on your running; we discuss several options for enhancing your performance in Part III, *Mind and Body*. We begin by encouraging you to stretch your mind with visualizations, then your body with two full-body stretching circuits. Stretching, weight-training and speed drills are the most obvious parts of training to run faster, but we've also included information on the role massage and relaxation can play in increasing your speed.

In Part IV, *Complementing Your Workout*, we discuss cross-training and provide information about four activities that will multiply the benefits you get from running alone. Since a strong 'core' improves your overall stability and running performance, we provide a core training circuit. We also encourage you to try weight-training for more power and strength, and pool running for its aerobic

and recuperative effects. Lastly, you get a primer on the benefits of stair climbing, which will supercharge your leg muscles and lungs for faster running overall.

We conclude with a comprehensive section on training entitled *Training for the Next Level*. Whether you're preparing for a 5-K, 10-K, half- or full marathon, you'll find a detailed training plan here to guide you through every week of your preparation. Each training plan includes a variety of workouts that will get you to the starting line in good shape to run your best race ever – or finish your first race with flying colours. In addition, we've included important information about injury troubleshooting and recovery, running camps and goal setting.

In this book, we want to guide your growth as an intermediate runner as positively as possible, with the information and advice you need to focus and organize your running goals, experiences and achievements.

Keep this book next to your training log to make sure you'll have all the information at your fingertips to push yourself to go out there and run faster. So what are you waiting for? Your best run is just around the corner.

PART I:
BACK TO BASICS

Meeting Your Goals

Don't put yourself on the outside track with unrealistic expectations.

As you progress as a runner, you expect to see results. The ability to run faster and for longer periods of time, generally at the same time, sums up most runners' expectations. But what happens when your improvement stalls? Whether you call it hitting a wall, reaching a training plateau, or just falling into a rut, these periods can be frustrating enough to cause a runner to give up. Here are five ways to get your running back on track.

Setting a *personal best*, or PB, is one sure way to pull yourself out of a running rut. But how do you reach that PB when you're stuck? Often, following more carefully the time-tested tenets of running will do the trick. At the very least, in order to improve – to run faster, that is – you'll need to understand and follow these rules of running:

Add Variety

Have you succumbed to the common mistake of doing the same old workout day in and day out? When your runs start to look like your commute to work – same path, every day – you've stopped challenging your body and mind with variety, which is essential for improvement. Vary locations, the types of workouts you do and even weekly plans, so that nothing becomes too familiar.

Cut Back

If you've been consistently increasing your distance from week to week, the rut you're in could be your body's way of saying *no more*. Reduce your distance by 25 to 50 percent for 1 week, and then resume where you left off the following week. The break you give your body will improve your running and your attitude.

Take a Break

Maybe cutting back won't quite cut it; perhaps the best thing for you is to take a longer break from running. A few weeks of various cross-training workouts will give your body and mind new challenges; at the end of your time off, start a new running programme. As they say, absence makes the heart grow fonder, and it's as true of running as it is of loved ones.

Alternate Hard and Easy

Hard days should really make you sweat, and easy days should be thought of as 'recovery' days. On your easy days, leave the stress and the pressure to excel behind, and just enjoy your runs at a slow pace, because that's the best way to recharge your resources for the next hard run.

Practise Patience

Long-time runners know that it takes the body time to adjust to the rigours of training, and they listen to the feedback their bodies provide, be it benign, like a plateau or more strident, like an injury. Patience, in other words, is a virtue, and you will profit from reminding yourself that all things will change over time – even a seemingly interminable rut.

Cycle Training

This book is all about giving you the tools to move beyond the basics of running. To do that, we offer a variety of regimes, from speed work programmes to cross-training plans. How do you fit all of these different types of training together into a single plan? It's called *cycle training*, a technique that helps you systematically incorporate different workouts into your training schedule to improve your running performance over a set period of time.

Start with a goal: a distance such as a 10-K, or a pace such as an 8-minute mile, for example. From there, you choose the best workouts (speed, hills, etc.) you need to do to reach your goal over a specific time frame, or cycle. Then, schedule these workouts over one or more 10-, 14- or 21-day cycles.

BENEFITS OF CYCLE TRAINING

Recovery and rest days are built into the schedule, so you're less likely to over-train.

Endurance and speed training are included in each cycle, so you benefit from both. That will improve your overall fitness, too.

Key workouts such as speed work, long runs and hill runs increase gradually in intensity over the course of the cycle. These are designed so you won't run out of steam too early in the process.

CREATE A PROGRAMME

Here's how to create your own cycle-training programme. Just follow these simple steps:

Choose a race that you want to run, making sure you have adequate time to train: 6 weeks for a 5-K, 9 weeks for a 10-K, 12 weeks for a half-marathon and 16 to 18 weeks for a marathon. Choose a cycle length: 14, 21, 28 days – as long as it works for you, it's your choice. Two 21-day cycles would work for a 5-K that is 6 weeks away.

Set a reasonable time goal for your race (based on your training runs) and, from that, figure out what your appropriate pace-per-mile should be. For example, if your time goal for a 5-K (3.1 mile) race is 26 minutes, your race pace per mile average would be 8 minutes, 23 seconds (26 ÷ 3.1 = 8.38 minutes or 8 minutes, 23 seconds).

Choose the number of key, or hard, workouts you'll do in the cycle. These include intervals, tempo runs, hill runs, and long runs. Four in a 21-day cycle is appropriate if you run 15 or fewer miles per week; 8 workouts would suit a runner who runs more than 35 miles (56.3 km) per week.

Choose the *kind* of key workouts you'll do – select at least two from the list above. Keep everything else easy: low-stress runs, cross-training and days off.

Develop your schedule so that the intensity of the key workouts increases over the course of the cycle. For example, begin with a long run, followed by a hill or tempo run, leading up to a more vigorous workout like track intervals as you complete the cycle.

Benchmark your efforts with a test at the end of every cycle to assess your progress. A 3-mile (4.8 km) timed run is a good option. Run mile 1 at a comfortable pace, mile 2 slightly faster and mile 3 at race pace.

Increase intensity for the next cycle in your schedule: Add 5 to 10 minutes to long runs; 1 to 2 repeats to hill and speed workouts; and 5 minutes to tempo runs. But taper before races: Skip long runs, and cut speed work and hill

Cycle training improves performance in all areas and helps keep things interesting.

repeats by half. Do this 3 to 4 days before a 5- or 10-K, a week or so before a half-marathon, and 2 or more weeks before a marathon.

To use cycle-training to reach a certain running pace within a certain time frame requires that you have realistic expectations: Think about improving your time in terms of seconds, not minutes, and be reasonable when choosing a time frame (for instance, 30 days rather than 1 week) and you will have a better chance of success.

Eat for Speed

You probably know by now that certain foods can have a strong effect – for better or worse – on your running. Having a slice of wholewheat bread with a slather of peanut butter an hour before you run can do wonders for your performance, whereas a pre-run doughnut can feel like a stone in your gut as you lope along. What exactly makes a food good fuel for running isn't always apparent, especially to beginner and intermediate runners. Here's the lowdown about the energy your body needs to run.

THE BASICS

Carbohydrates are your body's primary source of fuel and, despite the bad press they sometimes get, a vital component of a runner's diet. When you eat carbs, your body breaks them down into a simple sugar called *glucose*, and then stores it in your muscles as a fuel called *glycogen*. Your body prefers to burn glycogen over fat or protein as fuel, although it does use all three as fuel.

Proteins are metabolized more slowly than carbs, and provide an important source of energy for the body during runs that last an hour or more. Your body also uses protein to recover from training and to repair and build body tissue, especially muscle.

Fats form an essential part of your nutritional picture, and provide a solid energy base for low to medium-intensity workouts and endurance. Some fats are better for your body than others; those called monounsaturated are best because they lower the levels of 'bad' cholesterol (LDL) and raise the levels of 'good' (HDL) cholesterol in your blood – decreasing the risk of heart disease. They're found in olive oil, avocados and most nuts. Saturated fat, mostly found in animal products but also in palm and coconut oils, raise LDL levels, which increases the risk of heart disease. Trans-fats, sometimes referred to as hydrogenated fats, also raise LDL levels. Steer clear of the latter two types of fat in your diet.

SO, WHAT SHOULD I EAT?

A simple well-balanced runner's diet should be comprised of 60 percent carbohydrates, 15 percent protein, and 25 percent fat.

Runners need adequate protein and carbohydrates in their diets.

CALCULATE YOUR CALORIE INTAKE

To work out how many grams of carbohydrates you need each day, multiply your weight in pounds by 2.25. For protein and fat, multiply your weight by .56 and .41 respectively. (To convert your weight from kilograms to pounds multiply by 2.2.) Here are the calculations for a 120-pound runner who runs fewer than 30 miles per week:

120 x 2.25 = 270 grams carbohydrates

120 x .56 = 67.2 grams protein

120 x .41 = 49.2 grams fat

To calculate the total number of calories that a 120-pound runner needs to eat each day, you need to know that 1 gram of carbohydrate is 4 calories, 1 gram of protein is 4 calories and 1 gram of fat is 9 calories:

270 grams carbohydrates x 4 calories per gram = 1,080 calories from carbohydrates

67.2 grams protein x 4 calories per gram = 269 calories from protein

49.2 grams fat x 9 calories per gram = 443 calories from fats

TOTAL DAILY INTAKE: 1,792 CALORIES

Once you do these calculations, you can fine-tune your diet using the nutrition labels on the foods you buy; understanding these calculations will help you make better sense of food labels, too.

Calculate Your Calorie Intake on page 15 shows how to use those ratios to determine how many calories you need to consume each day.

A RUNNER'S SHOPPING LIST

Here are the foods to add to your shopping trolley the next time you head to the supermarket.

Eating healthfully is easier when you understand how it will improve your running.

Meat

Fresh or frozen fish, including trout, herring and salmon, is a great source of omega-3 fats – a heart-healthy fat. Also consider fresh, frozen or tinned prawns, scallops and crab. Lean cuts of meat – lamb chops, sirloin steak, pork tenderloin – are great picks, but be sure to trim the fat. Chicken and turkey are excellent sources of protein, but remove the skin to eliminate most of the fat. You can also eat processed meat that contains 3 or fewer grams of fat per serving – lean bacon and ham are good options. Vegetarians should check out soya meat substitutes such as burgers, sausages and tofu products.

Fruit and Vegetables

When it comes to produce, the more colourful the better. Spice up your fruit bowls with more than just apples, oranges and bananas: add in berries, plums and nectarines. The same principle applies to vegetables: aubergine, cabbage and Brussels sprouts are just a few of the vegetables to include in your diet.

Beans and Nuts

Beans are a terrific low-fat source of protein, and although nuts are higher in fat, these fats are unsaturated, making them a healthy choice.

Bread

Try to avoid white bread, which is made from less healthy processed flour, opting instead for whole-grain varieties or 100 percent wholewheat bread. The healthiest choices available are those that supply at least 2 grams of fibre per serving.

Dairy

Choose fat-free or low-fat milk, yogurt, buttermilk and chocolate milk. In addition, low-fat cottage cheese, cheddar, feta, Swiss, mozzarella, ricotta and cream cheeses are all good choices. Don't forget eggs, which are not only a nutrient-packed source of protein, but can also be prepared in a wide variety of ways.

Cereal

Both cold and hot cereals can be rich in carbohydrates, fibre and vitamins and minerals, and make a good start to the day. Your best bets are those whole-grain cereals that provide 5 grams or more of fibre in each serving.

THE BASICS

Here's how your shopping list matches up with the 3 sources of nutrition: carbohydrates, protein and fats.

Carbohydrates

apples	oranges	pears	nectarines
peaches	plums	bananas	grapefruit
melon	berries	pineapple	carrots
celery	cabbage	aubergine	onions

Protein

chicken	turkey	salmon	swordfish
herring	trout	bluefish	tuna
lean beef	lamb chops	pork	tofu
tempeh	soyabeans	legumes	cottage cheese

Fats

olive oil	rapeseed oil	flaxseed oil	avocados
almonds	soya oil	cashews	hazelnuts
peanuts	pistachios	olives	nut butters

Drink Up

Water covers more than 70 percent of the Earth's surface, and constitutes about 60 percent of your body mass. Without it, your body shuts down quickly – and even a decrease of only 1 to 2 percent can have a negative impact on your running performance.

Dehydration does more than make you thirsty. When you run, you sweat, and the fitter you are, the more you sweat. That's because a fit body is more effective at keeping itself cool, and since the evaporation of perspiration is how your body cools itself, more sweat means better cooling. A fit runner loses about a litre an hour during a hard run. Without enough water in your body, your blood thickens, your heart rate increases, your heart's pumping efficiency drops and your body temperature rises. In severe cases, you can literally sweat yourself right out of the ability to cool your body, which dramatically increases your risk of suffering heatstroke, a serious and potentially fatal condition.

HOW MUCH IS ENOUGH?

So how much do you really need to drink for optimal performance, let alone health? The old rule of '8 glasses per day' has lost credibility of late, given a lack of evidence for its efficacy. In fact, that one rule has contributed to a mania for hydration that many of us – runners and non-runners alike – struggle with to this day.

For moderately active men and women, there are new, gender-specific formulas for determining the best amount of fluids to drink throughout the day. For women, multiply your body weight in pounds by .31 to find the proper number of fluid ounces to drink; for men, use .35 as the multiplier. For example, a 183-pound man should drink 64 fluid ounces of water a day:

183 x 0.35 = 64 fluid ounces

A 129-pound woman, by contrast, should drink 40 ounces:

129 x 0.31 = 40 fluid ounces

To calculate using kilograms and millilitres, use the following formulas. For women, multiply your body weight in kilograms by .68 to find the number of millilitres; for men, use .77 as the multiplier.

How you drink is nearly as important as drinking enough. It would not do your body much good if you were to gulp down all of the water you need for the day in one sitting. Instead, drink small amounts of fluid frequently over the course of the day to maintain your body's hydration level. In addition, always drink a little past the feeling of thirst. Your body actually shuts off the thirst sensation before you've replenished lost fluids. Remember: If you're feeling thirsty, your body is already low on fluids, so drink consistently to keep your levels topped up.

BEYOND WATER

The variety of beverages geared specifically for athletes has increased dramatically over the past few years, and companies continue to develop more specialized drinks to meet the diverse needs of athletes and their varying workouts. So how do you know which, when and how much of what kind to drink? And do you really even need to drink any of these specialized sports drinks if you already drink appropriate amounts of water? Thanks to the recent research conducted on these beverages, the answers are now clearer than ever.

CLEAR AND COPIOUS

Tired of keeping track of how much water you've drunk in the day? Stop monitoring your intake and take a peek at your outflow. Your urine colour and frequency of urination can tell you a lot about your state of hydration. Pale yellow urine is a good sign that plenty of fluid is on board for waste excretion (but don't judge your urine colour within a few hours after taking vitamin supplements, since the unused vitamins, particularly the B vitamin riboflavin, turn your urine a bright yellow). Frequent urination is another good sign that you're getting enough fluid. In other words, if your urine is clear and copious, you're well hydrated.

GAUGE YOUR PERSPIRATION RATE

Knowing your perspiration rate helps you rehydrate appropriately during training and competition. Start by weighing yourself nude before a timed training run, and then again immediately afterwards. Every pound (0.45 kg) of lost weight means you've lost 1 pint (about 570 ml) of fluids; and generally, runners lose between 2 and 8 pints (1 to 1.75 litre) per hour.

For example, if you lose 2 pounds (0.9 kg) during an hour-long run, that's 2 pints (just over 1 litre) of lost water. You need ½ pint (240 ml) of fluid every 15 minutes while you're running. During runs that last for 1 hour or more, try a low-sugar, non-caffeinated sports beverage instead. You'll benefit from the easily assimilated carbs and electrolytes, and the flavour is refreshing. For runs that last less than an hour, stick with water.

Despite the fact that most runners know the importance of staying hydrated, many often routinely drink less than they ought to because of water's flavour – or rather, lack thereof. If you fall into this camp, sports drinks might be a good solution for you.

So what are the choices? For those who run for an hour or less, the so-called *fitness waters* provide a good alternative to water. These beverages lack the calories of sports drinks, an added benefit for those trying to lose weight, but come in a variety of flavours that make them more interesting than plain water. Often with fewer than 20 calories per 500 ml, fitness water usually provides a small but helpful amount of sodium and potassium, as well as B, C and E vitamins.

For runs lasting longer than an hour, and for those who sometimes experience nausea shortly after their long runs, finding a workable solution can be tricky. Eating carbohydrates after a run can eliminate the nausea, but to someone who is feeling ill, carbohydrates are unappealing. The development of carb-boosting recovery drinks, however, provides a good solution to this old problem. Unlike traditional sports drinks, these beverages usually contain 40 to 60 grams (1¼ to 2 ounces) of carbohydrates in an average 240-ml serving, which makes them a suitable drink during and after any intense, long run.

Ultra-runners, athletes who run distances longer than the traditional marathon, are more aware than ever of the main risk associated with *hyponatraemia*, a condition in which the blood is depleted of salts that is caused by drinking too much water – but only now are they becoming aware of the way that sports drinks can play a role in preventing the condition. Like water, these beverages keep a runner hydrated; however, unlike water, sports drinks also help maintain the body's levels of electrolytes (salts that your body needs) which become depleted during long runs – and so reversing the causes of hyponatraemia.

Long runs don't just deplete your body of salt and electrolytes; they also burn plenty of calories (120 to 240 per hour), and sports beverages also offer the caloric boost (in the form of carbohydrates that your body can easily digest) that your body requires to perform at its best.

Sports beverages might just improve your performance as well: In one recent study, athletes who drank a sports beverage actually ran faster and had significantly better endurance than those who drank a placebo.

THE TRUTH ABOUT CAFFEINE

Research conducted in the last 2 years has reversed the age-old myth that caffeinated beverages are diuretics. Research confirmed that caffeinated beverages have no more diuretic effect than plain old water. You drink a lot of water, you need to go to the toilet. Same with caffeinated beverages, no more, no less. So if you've always made time for a cup of coffee or tea an hour or so before you run, continue to enjoy it without worries. However, stay away from caffeine during or after your run so that you don't overstimulate your nervous system.

Try Some Variety

We started Part I with a discussion of running basics and an exploration of cycle training; we moved on to a review of nutrition fundamentals. We end with a word about your feet, or rather, what your feet run on – yet another elemental part of your running life.

Oddly enough, hard surfaces such as pavements and asphalt roads – while contributing to injuries – actually ease your running efforts. *Toe-offs* (the push that your toes give as your foot leaves the ground to stride forwards) get stronger on these surfaces due to the impact energy rebounding into your feet and calves. More yielding surfaces, such as grass, smooth dirt trails and foam and cinder tracks, may slow you down, but they offer a multitude of benefits, including a better workout for the stabilizing muscles of your torso, which must work to keep you upright on an uneven surface; less stress on the joints of your legs and feet; and stronger *proprioception* (your feet's ability to adjust to uneven terrain), leading to stronger ankles and reduced risk of sprains.

So should you do all your training off-road? Not unless it really appeals to you, as it does to some runners. The best way to protect your body (and to stave off possible boredom) is to include a variety of surfaces in your day-to-day training regime.

GOING BAREFOOT

Some professional runners run barefoot while training and competing, crediting it with increasing their speed. If you want to give it a try, start very gradually, walking barefoot outside a half-hour per day. You'll need to spend several weeks toughening the soles and muscles of your feet before attempting to run barefoot. When you do run, start on smooth grass or packed sand at the beach. Build distance and speed gradually, and always watch for litter and sharp objects that might cause injury.

PART II:
SPEED WORK ESSENTIALS

Running Faster

Even when you race, beating your best time may matter more than crossing the finish line before others.

You've been running for a while now, and maybe you've even competed in a race. Your confidence has grown; no longer do you worry about whether you'll finish – now you worry about how *well* you'll finish.

You're curious about what you can do to go faster. The answer: Speed work. Speed work involves running at a faster than normal pace (or at a certain percentage of your maximum heart rate) for specific periods of time (10 minutes, for example, at a 5-K race pace) or under specific conditions (up a hill, for instance). Running fast exercises your heart intensely, making it pump more efficiently over time. That means if you perform speed work diligently, you will be able to run faster times at a lower heart rate. Since hard running inevitably brings you past the point at which lactic acid – the waste product generated by your muscles as they burn fuel – builds up in your blood, becoming faster at lower levels of cardiovascular effort is a godsend to your performance. (See *Tempo Runs*, pages 34–35, for more information.)

Introduce your body to speed work gradually – and take your recovery days seriously – and you'll reap benefits for many years to come. The workouts described in this section are presented in order of increasing intensity: fartleks, hill running, tempo runs and interval training. We recommend you start your speed training with fartleks, then, after a couple of weeks, work in some hill running, and then gradually move up to interval repeats.

Also in Part II you'll find some tips on improving your form (which will make you a faster, more efficient runner) along with some information about every speed work enthusiast's most indispensable tool, the heart-rate monitor. So read on, lace up your shoes and give it all a go.

LEARN THE LINGO

Throughout Part II, you'll see references to words and phrases that may be unfamiliar. We'll highlight those in special boxes.

- **Race pace** The pace (expressed in minutes and seconds) you would run a given race distance – for example an 8 minute-per-mile pace for a 5-K race, or a 9:30 pace for a 10-K. Your race pace depends on the race you're training for, and is unique to your level of conditioning; most runners also use their race pace as a target for training leading up to a particular competition.
- **Maximum heart rate** Often abbreviated MHR, this is the fastest rate (per minute) at which your heart can beat. This number remains relatively stable and is not affected by your level of fitness. Different workouts are performed at different percentages of your MHR. You'll read more about this on pages 28 and 29.

The Perfect Form

Developing good running form is worthy of any runner's attention, especially since it will benefit you in your speed training, your racing and your everyday running. When you run with proper form, you run efficiently – with no wasted effort. From top to bottom, here are the basics.

Head

Hold it upright, without leaning forwards at the neck. Imagining your head being stretched upwards from the crown slightly may help you to maintain your head's steady alignment over your body.

Torso and Shoulders

Hold your torso upright, with your back and shoulders relaxed. The more relaxed your shoulders, the more relaxed you'll feel overall. Conversely, fatigue or discomfort can cause you to hunch your shoulders, which will tend to make you stoop forwards from the hips, placing strain on your knees.

Arms

Easy, flowing movement is key. Keep your elbows bent at 90 degrees, and swing your arms back-and-forth from the shoulders.

STRIDE LENGTH

Your feet should land directly under your body's centre of gravity. From the side, this means your lower leg (below the knee) is not stretched out in front of you at the point of footfall, but rather under you, with your knee slightly bent for optimal flexing later in the stride. From the front, your foot should be placed more or less under your body's midline, so as to minimize side stresses on your knees.

Keep your feet under you in this manner, and your stride will be well suited for speedy running over long distances. Although sprinters stretch their strides to the maximum, that running form is ideal for, well, sprinting, and is inefficient for distances beyond half a mile or so. Long strides? Leave them to the pros.

Keep your arms from swinging in front of your torso excessively; arm-crossover can sometimes twist your spine unnecessarily.

Hands
Held loosely cupped in front of your arms is best. Imagine yourself holding a raw egg and you'll see what we mean. Clenched fists are both a sign and a cause of tension.

Hips
Your hips are your centre of gravity, so they're key to proper form. With your torso and back upright and straight, your hips naturally fall into proper alignment. When gauging the position of your hips, think of your pelvis as a bowl filled with water; try not to spill any of it.

Thighs
Distance runners (unlike sprinters) do not need to lift their thighs excessively to achieve an efficient stride. All you need is a slight lift to get the leg moving forwards.

Feet
Keep your feet relaxed and loose, and landing directly under your centre of gravity (this minimizes side-stress on your knees).

Paying attention to your running form can reduce the risk of injury.

Heart-Rate Training

Runners tend to avoid the gear and gimmicks that dominate other sports. Just give us decent shoes and an open trail, and we're off. Sometimes, however, it really is all about the equipment, and heart-rate monitors are a case in point. If you want to boost your training to the next level, a heart-rate monitor will help you do just that.

Your heart rate, the number of times your heart beats in 1 minute, provides an objective gauge of how hard you're working, one that is almost always more accurate than your own perception of how hard you're working. So no matter what type of runner you are, beginner, intermediate or advanced – a heart-rate monitor will help you train and improve more effectively.

Heart-rate monitors designed for runners generally consist of 2 to 3 parts: an elasticized band that fits around your chest that monitors your heart rate; a wristwatch that receives a radio signal from the chest monitor displaying your pulse rate; and in some a GPS (Global Positioning Satellite) transponder that calculates your distance travelled through triangulation with a satellite in orbit.

Some monitors also come with software that enables you to upload your workout data into your computer so that you can analyze your training (pace, heart rate, distances run) with tools including graphs and spreadsheets. However, almost all models log several workouts' worth of data in the wristwatch and issue a tone when your heart rate is either higher or lower than the range you've specified.

Nifty gadgets, such as this wristwatch heart monitor, make it easy to gauge your workout.

HEART-RATE TRAINING

To get the best benefit from your speed work (and in fact all your runs) you need to run in the appropriate heart rate zone. To use this training method, you need to calculate your maximum heart rate (MHR). Use the following formula to do that:

$$MHR = 208 - (0.7 \times your\ age)$$

So, if you're 40 years old:

$$MHR = 208 - (0.7 \times 40)$$
$$MHR = 208 - 28$$
$$MHR = 180$$

This formula indicates that 180 is the maximum number of times a 40-year-old's heart is able to beat in 1 minute. Once you know your MHR, you can calculate your training heart rate zones:

For easy and long runs: 65 to 75 percent of your MHR

In the case of our theoretical runner:

$$0.65 \times 180 = 117$$
$$0.75 \times 180 = 135$$

In other words, on easy and long runs, our runner's heart rate should stay between 117 and 135 beats per minute (BPM), or between 20 and 23 beats every 10 seconds. Here are the percentages for your other training runs:

Tempo Runs: 87 to 92 percent of MHR
Intervals: 95 to 100 percent of MHR

For races, aim to keep your heart rate in the following ranges:

5-K: 95 to 97 percent of MHR
10-K: 92 to 94 percent of MHR

Fartleks

If you don't speak any Swedish, let us teach you your first phrase: *fartlek*, a compound word meaning 'speed play'. Fartlek workouts are a great way for the uninitiated to get into speed work. All it requires is that you vary your pace during your run, based on how you feel. Feel like racing to that tree over there? Go for it. Want to jog to the base of that hill beyond the tree? Excellent idea.

By varying speed and running intensity constantly throughout your run, fartleks never give your body a chance to acclimatize to a particular level of effort. Your muscles, lungs, and mind are constantly challenged. Fartlek training works on the basis of *perceived effort* – you change pace when you feel the time is right.

Fartleks can turn even a hard workout into an (almost) enjoyable experience.

FARTLEK BASICS

These are the rules of fartlek training; keep them in mind as you plan your workouts:

Alternate hard-effort running with slower, recovery-paced jogging or walking intervals.

Run at least 50 percent of your fartlek distance at race pace or faster.

Include all types of movement in your fartlek workouts, from jogging and recovery-paced walking to sprinting.

Put in a good effort: Having no set structure to follow is certainly not a valid excuse for taking it easy.

THREE FARTLEK WORKOUTS

Speed Up, Slow Down

After warming up as usual, find some hilly, rolling terrain for your run. Increase your tempo on the inclines, and take it easy down the descents. Aim for 30 minutes of continuous running.

Follow the Leader

Do your fartlek workout with a group, and give each person a set number of minutes (3 to 5) to set the group's training pace.

Catch the Rabbit

With a group of runners, imagine that you are a bunch of starving hunter-gatherers chasing a rabbit; sometimes you sprint after it, and sometimes you sneak up on it. One person 'sees' the rabbit, then sets the direction and the pace towards the designated landmark. 'The rabbit is right behind that tree.' Another runner 'sees' the rabbit at that point, and so on.

Runners swear by the effectiveness of fartlek training. Not only does it build endurance and balance the development of fast- and slow-twitch muscles in your legs (see below), but it demands that you pay close attention to your breathing and how you feel while running. When 'play' is part of the name, you know it's fun, but it's good for you, too, so include fartleks in your training once a week and reap the benefits.

LEARN THE LINGO

Our muscles are made up of two different types of fibres: slow-twitch and fast-twitch.

- **Slow-twitch** muscle fibres are good for endurance activities like distance running. They receive more oxygen from the blood, and can hold contractions for longer periods of time before getting tired, resulting in prolonged strength.
- **Fast-twitch** muscle fibres are built for expending extreme amounts of power for short periods of time. They're good for fast movements such as sprinting, but fatigue quickly.

Each of us has both fast- and slow-twitch fibres in each muscle, but some people have a higher ratio of one type of muscle, making them better at either sprinting or distance running.

Hills

For a challenging change of pace, head for the hills.

Hill running – also known as 'speed work in disguise' – is about increasing your lung efficiency, muscle strength and overall endurance. No, hills aren't fun. But incorporating hill running into your training programme will make them much more manageable come race day. Not only that, but it will make you a faster runner, too.

Hill running is an intense workout that exercises your quadriceps (the large muscles on the front of your thighs) and joints like nothing else, so do only one session a week. Soon you'll be running faster and easier on hills and flat terrain, with decidedly more spring in your stride. Try these workouts to get you started.

Short Hill Repeats
Find a hill that is between 100 and 200 metres (109 to 218 yds) long. Do 1 or 2 sets of 10 runs up the hill at a fast pace, followed by a slow recovery jog back down. You'll be working *very* hard, but since the distance is short, you won't be exhausting yourself; in fact, you will be improving your

performance during short- to middle-distance races, from 1.5 km (1 mile) to a 5-K (3.1 miles).

Push on the Uphills

Incorporate this approach in your middle- to long-distance training runs, up to 16 km (10 miles) or so. Whenever you hit an incline, push yourself harder, then recover on the flat and downhill stretches.

Medium-Length Circuits

This workout requires a specific course, but once you're able to do it, you'll find it worth the effort. Find a hill that is about 440 m (¼ mile)

Hill running isn't always fun, but we guarantee that it will make you a stronger, faster runner.

long, followed by a flat stretch of approximately 1 km (about ⅔ of a mile) and ending in 800 m (½ mile) moderate downhill that returns to your starting point. Run up the hill, recover on the flat section at the top and then run back downhill at a fast-but-relaxed pace.

HILL POINTERS

- Spring or bounce up the hills to build your calf muscles.
- Pump your arms only if necessary when you need to gain momentum; otherwise, it wastes energy. Instead, concentrate on maintaining proper form.
- Try to stay upright as you move up each hill, but also make it a point to lean forwards slightly on those downhill stretches.
- Tackle steeper and longer hills gradually. Your confidence will increase each time you master a more difficult hill, and that will reinforce the notion that, given time and commitment, there is nothing you won't be able to do.

Tempo Runs

Tempo running may be the perfect workout. It trains your body to run at faster speeds before lactic acid (the waste product produced by muscles as they burn fuel) builds up in your blood and slows you down with that tired, heavy-legged feeling.

The point at which this happens is called your *lactate threshold*, or LT, and it's unique to your personal physiology. Most runners reach their LT while running at between 85 and 92 percent of their maximum heart rate (see page 29). The pace at which you reach your LT is called your *tempo pace*. Pushing yourself to run at this pace for 20 to 35 minutes will, over time, make your heart and lungs more efficient. In turn, this will allow you to run harder before you reach your LT.

FIND YOUR TEMPO PACE

A heart-rate monitor (see pages 28–29) will help you stay at your LT during tempo runs; if you don't have one, use one of these methods to find your tempo pace.

Pace

'Comfortably hard' basically means that you are working hard but can still maintain that pace for 40 to 45 minutes. If you tried to talk at this pace, you could utter a few words at a time, but couldn't hold a conversation.

Breathing

Running at or near your LT generally requires an efficient breathing pattern such as inhaling for 2 strides and exhaling for 1 stride.

Compared to Race Pace

If you've run a race recently, use that pace to help you find your tempo pace. Reduce your per-mile pace by about 30 seconds from your 5-K pace, or 20 seconds from your 10-K pace.

TEMPO WORKOUTS

Try these tempo run workouts, bracketed by your usual warm-up and cool-down.

Tempo on the Track

If you've never tried a tempo run before, this is a great one to start with. Run six 1,000-metre (0.62

Tempo running will strengthen your heart and lungs and improve your endurance.

miles) repeats on the track at tempo pace with 1-minute recovery jogs/walks in between. Add 1 repeat per week until you can run 8 to 10 repeats comfortably.

Basic Tempo

Run at tempo pace for 20 to 35 minutes (or 2 to 4 miles [3.2 to 6.4 km] if you prefer to work with distance). If you can go further than 4 miles (6.4 km) in 35 minutes, break up your tempo mid-run with a 45-second recovery jog.

Sandwich Tempo

Run for 15 minutes at tempo pace, then jog at recovery pace for 5 to 7 minutes before returning to your tempo pace for another 15 minutes.

Of the three tempo workouts described here, this one is the most challenging, since the second tempo run presents you with greater effort in the face of greater fatigue. On the plus side, this workout is a terrific aerobic conditioner, so it's worth the effort.

Interval Training

Tempo runs bring you to the LT and hold you there, improving how your body uses oxygen during exercise over time, but interval training sends you over the LT repeatedly, with the goal of training your whole body to run much, much faster.

The benefits of *interval training*, or alternating running hard and running easy for short distances, are myriad. First, when you run the same pace, distance, and/or route day to day, your body grows accustomed to your workout; that can contribute to hitting a training plateau. Interval training shakes your body out of that rut, recruits more fast-twitch muscle fibres (see *Learn the Lingo*, page 31), and stimulates the motor nerve cells in the spinal cord that activate them, meaning that you become able to run faster more easily. Interval training also results in faster leg turnover and stronger legs, and increases your heart's ability to pump oxygen-rich blood and your muscle's ability to use that blood.

Interval training is also a great all-round body strengthener, and despite the stresses it places on the body, is not a common cause of injury, so you can work intervals into your training programme without fears of getting sidelined.

RULES OF INTERVAL TRAINING

Complete no more than 1 session of interval runs per week.

Warm up first with a 3-km (2-mile) jog before the workout. After, transition from the warm-up jog and recovery walk/jog, then start the interval training with 4 to 6 100-metre (approximately 109 yds) strides (running fast).

Never sprint all-out.

Keep moving, walking or jogging between intervals; this 'active recovery' allows your heart rate to come down a bit.

End your interval workout before you're exhausted; you should feel that you could do more. You may need to stop your workout before you've completed the prescribed number of repeats; that's fine, do as many as you can, and then work your way up.

THE WORKOUT

The variety of interval workouts is limited only by your imagination, but the following are some tried-

and-tested options. For the first 4 workouts, you'll need to locate a 400-metre (¼-mile) track.

100-Metre Breakdown

For this workout on a 400-metre (¼-mile) track, you'll speed through the 100-metre (approximately 109-yd) straight sections and recover by jogging on the curves. Before running this course initially,

If you hit a plateau, interval training can help you get over the hump.

calculate the following times for yourself, since they'll help determine the repeats you'll run: time yourself on a 1-lap run at an all-out race pace. Divide this number by 4 to get your 100-metre target time for the *last* set of repeats you'll run. Add 8 seconds to this number to get your 100-metre time for the *first* set of repeats you'll run.

This is a progressive workout, during which you start slow and end fast. If your 400-metre time is 1 minute, 30 seconds (1:30), your final repeat time should be about 23 seconds (1:30 ÷ 4), and you should run your first repeat in 31 seconds (23 + 8).

All repeats are run in pairs, so you'll run 100 metres on the straight, recover on the curve, run another 100 metres on the other straight, and return to your starting point after recovering on the second curve. One set of repeats will take you through one lap of the track. Here's the whole workout broken down by sets of repeats. Finish this interval workout with an adequate cool-down after the final repeat in set 5.

Set 1 Final repeat time + 8 seconds
Set 2 Final repeat time + 6 seconds
Set 3 Final repeat time + 4 seconds
Set 4 Final repeat time + 2 seconds
Set 5 Final repeat time

PICK IT UP

These 2 workouts teach you how to speed things up in a controlled manner.

Fast Finish 600s: Run 1 lap (400 m, ¼ mile) at a comfortable pace, followed by ½ lap (200 m, 218 yds) at the pace you would a 1-mile (1.6 km) race. Repeat 3 to 5 times with 3 minutes of recovery jogging between each 600 m set.

Drop-Down Tempo Run: Run 6 to 8 miles (10 to 13 km), starting slowly and dropping the pace 10 seconds per mile every mile so that the last mile is run at 10-K race pace.

Mile Breakdown

For this particular workout you'll need to know your 5-K race pace (See *Know Your Pace*, opposite page). Here's the breakdown in the form of four sets:

Set 1 4 laps (1,600 m) at your 5-K pace

Set 2 3 laps (1,200 m) at 1 to 2 seconds faster than your 5-K pace

Set 3 2 laps (800 m) at 3 to 4 seconds faster than your 5-K pace

Set 4 1 lap (400 m) at 5 to 6 seconds faster than your 5-K pace

If you're tapering for a race on the weekend, use this workout as your speed workout early in the week, but rein yourself in at your 5-K pace on all but the 400 m lap, when you can increase your speed to 5 to 6 seconds faster than your planned race pace.

The Circuit

For this challenging workout, you need to know your 10-K race pace (slightly slower than your 5-K pace, but still in tempo-run territory). Here's the circuit:

Set 1 1 ½ laps (600 m) at your 10-K pace

Set 2 100 metres at jogging recovery pace (one during which you could hold a conversation with a running partner)

Set 3 ½ lap (200 m) at just shy of an all-out sprint pace

Set 4 1 lap (400 m) at jogging recovery pace

The first few times you do this workout, start slowly with just 2 to 3 circuits, and then gradually work up to 4 or 5. If you want to increase your effort, stretch the 1½-lap set to 2 laps and the ½-lap section to 1½ laps.

The Negative Pyramid

This workout requires a 400-metre (¼-mile) track, a strong base of aerobic fitness and a dose of

KNOW YOUR PACE

The only way to learn how to pace yourself is to practise running a specific distance at a specific pace. Then you can extrapolate appropriate paces for any distance. This workout features lots of short-distance repeats to teach you the feel of your 10-K race pace.

mental toughness. Keep in mind that this workout will deplete your reserves, so do it only once every 3 to 4 weeks, and go easy for a few days afterwards.

> 2 laps (400 m) at 1 to 2 seconds slower than your 5-K pace, followed by a 2 lap recovery jog
>
> 3/4 lap (300 m) at your 5-K pace, followed by a 300-metre recovery jog
>
> ½ lap (200 m) at 1 to 2 seconds faster than your 5-K pace, followed by a 200-metre recovery jog
>
> ¼ lap (100 m) at just shy of an all-out sprint, followed by a 100-metre recovery jog.

That's one set; do three sets for a full workout. If you're fit, willing and able to do more, jog 1 lap (400 m) after the third set, then do a fourth and possibly even a fifth set before going straight to your cool-down.

The Quickie
Use this workout when you need to get in your intervals but you're pressed for time. It should take roughly 15 minutes total, and you don't need a track. Don't neglect your warm-up and cool-down.

15 repeats of 40 seconds at your 5-K pace, alternating with 20-second jog recoveries.

Repeat Quarters: Run up to 16 x 400 metres at 10-K race pace with 30 seconds recovery. When you slow down by more than 2 seconds from 10-K race pace, end the quickie workout.

Always pay close attention to your pace.

Putting It All Together

Don't let any single training session overshadow the big picture.

With all of the different ways you can train – from easy long runs to heart-pounding intervals – how do you put it all together? We talked earlier about scheduling your workouts in cycles. In this section, we pull our perspective back a bit further and talk about the even bigger chunks of time that make up training macrocycles and mesocycles.

These cycles form the basis of *periodization*, a form of goal-oriented training: You decide which races are important to you, and organize your training calendar so you'll be in top shape for those events. This is done by dividing the year into 'periods'. During each period, a specific type of training is empha-sized. Each period builds on the preceding one, letting you reach a time-targeted peak in fitness that would otherwise be impossible.

USING PERIODIZATION

Decide how many times you want to reach top performance in a year. If you're training for one major peak – a big competition such as a marathon – your entire year could be one macrocycle (a long period of time). Similarly, if you wanted to compete in a spring *and* an autumn marathon, you'd work with two macrocycles.

Each macrocycle should then be divided into several smaller periods of time (or mesocycles), lasting from 3 weeks to 3 months, during which you focus on sharpening specific skills. A 6-month macrocycle, for example, might be structured as follows:

Resting Mesocycle

This 3- to 4-week mesocycle of active rest will leave you physically and psychologically recovered from the previous season. During this active rest cycle, all running should be eliminated except for occasional light jogging. Don't panic – you can still cross-train lightly. During this time, enjoy activities you might have neglected during peak training times.

Aerobic Mesocyle

During this 8- to 12-week phase, running volume is emphasized over intensity. Focus on lots of steady-state runs, long runs and the occasional tempo run or longer, slow intervals.

Strength Mesocycle

During this 6- to 8-week long cycle, you continue the aerobic mesocycle, but add tempo runs, hill runs or longer intervals done at 5-K race pace once or twice a week. Intensity increases but overall distance stays constant.

Anaerobic Mesocycle

This 4- to 6-week cycle features the addition of shorter intervals run at mile race pace or faster. Make sure to fully recover between these repeats and maintain form. Continue with tempo runs and long intervals, but decrease your overall mileage.

Competition Mesocycle

Continue to reduce your overall mileage during this 4- to 6-week-long period, but keep up the intensity. Do hard workouts early in the week to allow for ample recovery before weekend races. By the end of this period, your race should become your main training stimulus as you approach peak performance.

Putting periodization to work for you – whether it's to train for two marathons in 1 year or for one 5-K that's just 6 weeks away, will markedly improve your running performance.

SPEED WORK TIPS

These speed work rules will help you as you train and get faster.

Train for Speed Once a Week

Even one session a week will dramatically increase leg turnover, and your speed in all race distances.

Never Train to Exhaustion

End your workout before you feel exhausted – leave some in the tank.

Be Patient

It may take 3 or 4 workouts before you settle in and feel comfortable running fast. And it will take 8 to 10 sessions before you see improved race times.

Train with Others

Don't jump into high-speed workouts alone, unless you're the type who responds well to solo effort. Rather, go out and find a partner.

Change Direction

When you run on a track or an inclined or cambered surface, such as a road, switch directions often to work your muscles evenly.

Warm Up Well

Breaking into a sprint or even a faster-than-usual run without first warming up invites injury.

Increase Repeats Gradually

When starting any speed work training regime, start with fewer rather then more repeats. Increasing gradually will ensure that you don't end up injured.

Run Through the Finish

Don't slow down as you approach the end of your hill, repeat or tempo run. Always run strong right through the finish.

Mind your Form

Poor form makes you susceptible to injury and wastes energy.

Alternate Workouts

Alternate easy and hard workouts and take rest days – they're especially important as you increase the intensity of your training.

Keeping your goals in mind will make reaching the finish line even easier.

PART III:
MIND AND BODY

Visualization

We talk a lot about physical fitness, and sometimes we even talk about mental toughness – the cultivated ability to push yourself further, faster, the way you do in speed work. But what about the other, more supple capacities of the mind? Don't overlook this powerful ally as you train – it can make the difference between success and failure.

Your imagination has no limits; you can picture yourself as an Olympic runner, surging out of the pack to grab the gold in the 5,000-metre race. You can imagine you're an intrepid ultra-marathoner, crossing whatever terrain you encounter with a combination of lithe strength and indomitable will. Cultivate the courage to imagine big, and do it regularly.

POSITIVE MIND

Involve as many of your senses as you can while engaging in visualization. See, hear, smell, feel and taste the sensation of running faster, for example. Use verbal affirmations to lock in these visualizations, so that when you say to yourself, 'I am a fast runner', you trigger your fully imagined visualization.

Just like any other habit, frequent use of your imagination leads to ease and facility in your imaginings and daydreams.

VISUALIZING SUCCESS

The power of visualization has been proven in scientific research. Imagining success and feelings of strength can train your body to respond positively through mimicry. Consider this progression of thoughts and their corresponding neuromuscular effects:

You have an image of an elite runner in your mind, striding confidently and strongly with perfect form and easy breathing.

By visualizing yourself running like this elite athlete, you train your muscles to act in that same fashion.

You effectively mimic what you imagine in your running. Harness your brain's capacity to dream in the service of your running, and you will improve faster

The power of positive thinking – visualizing success can make it easier to reach your goals.

and more completely. Imagining yourself in different situations such as trailing the race leader when in fact you're just a short distance behind someone on the park trail, can help you tap into energy for greater performance.

RACE PREPARATION

Mental preparation for a race is simple and effective; just follow these guidelines:

Run the course If possible, run the race course 1 to 2 times a month. If you live far away from the course, train on similar terrain to familiarize yourself.

See yourself succeed Visualize yourself feeling confident and strong as you run the course.

CHECK YOUR PROGRESS

Here's a workout idea that will engage both the conscious and subconscious parts of your mind, and double as a performance check, to boot.

Find a course or distance you can run once a month as a time-trial; use your visualization techniques to imagine yourself running it well. Gauge your progress each time you run it, in terms of stamina, speed and perceived effort. Each week, run one section of your time-trial course during an interval workout. After you've run the course completely via the sections, run it entirely on another day and compare your times to assess your progress.

Stretching for Speed

Stretching takes many forms. The older, discredited type called ballistic stretching, in which you use the weight of your body to repeatedly and forcefully stretch your body past its comfort limits, has given way to static stretching. Also called static-passive stretching, this type encourages you to stretch out muscles slowly, over 10 to 30 seconds at a time, by reaching a point of stretch and holding it. For an introduction to basic stretching for runners, see one of our other books – *Runner's World Best: Getting Started*. The following stretching routines build on those workouts.

STATIC-PASSIVE STRETCHING

The stretches we're presenting in this book are a bit more complex, but they are still considered static-passive which are stretches you gradually ease into. One stretch requires a belt or towel, and several more can be easily performed with a wall or pole handy.

The most innovative aspect of this section is that the stretches are presented as a circuit. With time and practice, you should be able to flow from one stretch to the next, ending with the well-known yoga pose, Downward Facing Dog.

Taken together, you have the foundation for a course of daily stretching that will keep you limber, flexible and relaxed for years to come.

DYNAMIC FLEXIBILITY

Dynamic flexibility is an alternative to static stretching. As the name suggests, movement is at the centre of dynamic flexibility exercises. In short, you will perform a series of quick movements that mimic the way your muscles and connective tissues stretch while running.

These drills are performed with controlled, low-to-no-load movements, as opposed to ballistic stretching, in which you use the weight of your body to force a muscle beyond its normal range of motion.

There is a large body of physiologic research to suggest that performing these movements improves your running by aligning muscle and fascial fibres so they slide against one another more easily (also known as reducing 'muscle friction'). Since the flexibility of a muscle or joint is specific to the motion and posture of the movement you're making, dynamic flex drills tend to be performed on your feet so that you are able to maximize the training effects in the same natural upright posture you adopt for running. In other words, you're basically enhancing your kinesthenic, or 'muscle' memory through dynamic flexibility exercises.

Stretching can not only increase speed, but reduce the chance of injury as well.

Static-Passive Stretches

Perform these stretches – after your run – in the order presented. Where necessary, repeat the stretch for the opposite leg or hip. From start to finish, this routine should take you about 10 to 15 minutes to accomplish.

HAMSTRINGS #1

Lie on your back with your left leg straight out. While keeping your left leg extended, bend your right knee and pull it into your chest by clasping your right leg.

HAMSTRINGS #2

While still on your back, extend your right leg straight out and bring your left knee into your chest. Hook a jump rope, long towel or belt around the bottom of your left foot. Slowly straighten your left leg and extend upwards to the limit of your stretch, and hold steady.

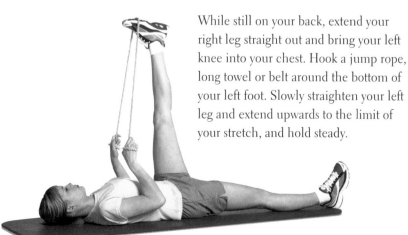

OUTER HIPS #1

Continue lying on your
back. Bend both knees and
place the outer side of your
left foot over your right
thigh, just above your knee.
Wrap your hands around
your right knee.

OUTER HIPS #2

Still lying on your back, extend both legs
straight out. Pull your right knee into your
chest. Grasp the outer side of your right knee
with your left hand and pull the knee across
your body towards the ground. Try to keep your
right arm extended with your shoulders and
head flat on the ground.

QUADRICEPS #1

Roll over onto your left side, and prop yourself up on your left forearm. Reach back with your right hand and grab your right foot. Press your right foot down towards your buttocks, while keeping your left hip on the ground. Don't arch your back or twist your pelvis.

QUADRICEPS #2

You can also do the quadriceps stretch while standing. For balance, rest your right hand on a wall, tree or fence. Grab your left foot with your left hand. While keeping the thigh muscles of your right leg tight, pull your left knee back and up towards your buttocks. Don't tilt forwards.

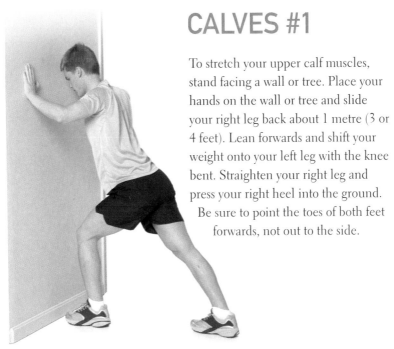

CALVES #1

To stretch your upper calf muscles, stand facing a wall or tree. Place your hands on the wall or tree and slide your right leg back about 1 metre (3 or 4 feet). Lean forwards and shift your weight onto your left leg with the knee bent. Straighten your right leg and press your right heel into the ground. Be sure to point the toes of both feet forwards, not out to the side.

CALVES #2

To stretch your lower calf muscles, assume the same position against the tree or wall. Slide your right leg back 60–90 cm (2–3 feet). Bend your left knee while keeping your right heel anchored to the ground. Bend your left knee to about the same position as the previous calf stretch.

LOWER BACK AND SHOULDERS

Stand with your feet about 15 cm (6 in) apart and about 1 metre (3 feet) away from a wall, fence, tree or other supporting surface of about shoulder height. Place both your hands about shoulder-width apart on the supporting surface, and flex forwards at your hips. Press down on the surface, flatten your back and lower your head between your arms.

DOWNWARD FACING DOG

First, crouch on all fours with hands and feet placed shoulder-width apart. Move your feet back another 15 cm (6 inches) or so. Press down into your feet, lift your knees off the ground and straighten your legs. Lift your buttocks high. Press firmly with your hands into the ground. Lower your heels towards the ground. Lengthen your back. Allow your head to hang freely.

Dynamic Flexibility

Because these dynamic flexibility drills will warm up your muscles, you can incorporate them safely into your pre-run warm-up 2 to 3 times a week.

ARM SWINGS

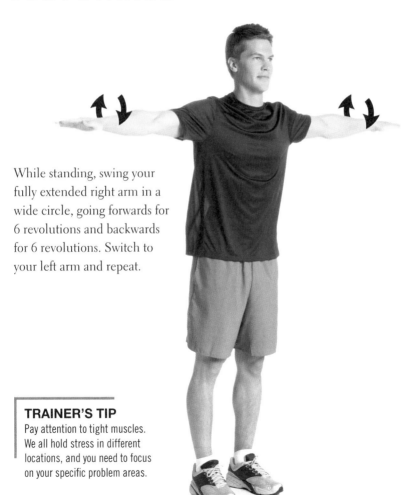

While standing, swing your fully extended right arm in a wide circle, going forwards for 6 revolutions and backwards for 6 revolutions. Switch to your left arm and repeat.

TRAINER'S TIP
Pay attention to tight muscles. We all hold stress in different locations, and you need to focus on your specific problem areas.

LEG SWINGS

Stand up straight with your hands on your hips. While standing on your right leg, swing your left leg back and forth in an exaggerated motion for 10 reps, then change position to swing your right leg. If needed, place your free hand on a wall for support.

ANKLE BOUNCE

Lean forwards against a wall with your feet close together and flat on the ground. Raise your heels as high as you can, then bounce them off the ground 20 times.

BICYCLE KICKS

Lie on your back and lift your legs and torso into the air, bracing your trunk with your lower arms as your weight rests on your shoulders and upper arms. Do 10 large scissor kicks with your outstretched legs, then switch to 10 'Y' scissor kicks out to the sides.

REMEMBER TO BREATHE

Breathing is fundamental when stretching and will help to further increase your flexibility. Take slow, calm breaths, inhaling through your nose, expanding your abdomen and exhaling slowly through your mouth. This will increase the oxygen content of the blood in your body, helping you to press further into your stretch. Breathing will also help to remove unwanted acid build-up in the muscles and will further help to relax your body after a great run.

Your body works hard and deserves to be rewarded. Massage is the perfect treat.

MASSAGE

Sports massage is integral to a whole-body approach to training, especially for injury rehabilitation or recovery. Like stretching, some of the benefits of massage are obvious, others more subtle. Massages generally feel great and relax your body and mind. For runners, massage offers some specific benefits:

- It flushes out the lactic acid that is produced as waste by your muscles when you run. This waste can build up in your muscles and cause soreness over time. Massage removes the acid which helps to speed recovery and increase flexibility, both of which can improve your performance.
- Massage therapy also works on a psychological level. In addition to simply relaxing you and clearing

waste from your muscles, it helps your entire body perform at its best. When your body functions at an optimal level, you feel more confident and that can improve your running form.

How often should you have a massage? It's up to you. For some runners, once every 6 weeks is enough. Just be sure to never get a deep sports massage less than 48 hours before a race, and allow at least 2 hours after a race to indulge in your next deep tissue massage.

To find a sports massage therapist, ask a running friend for a referral. Although you can find a massage therapist through an organization or online directory, word of mouth is the most effective way. For best results, work with a specialist in sports massage.

PART IV:
COMPLEMENTING YOUR WORKOUT

Complete Your Conditioning

Running is one of the best exercises, but it doesn't give you a full-body workout. Running focuses on your legs, causing some muscular imbalances. That's why cross-training is so important. To complement your running programme, we recommend you incorporate one or all of the workouts that appear on the following pages into your fitness regime.

CORE FITNESS

One of running's limitations is that it doesn't fully work your 'core' – the muscles of your back and abdominals that stabilize your spine, keep you upright, and (when they're strong) prevent injury to the lower back and hips. The benefits of a strong core include the following:

• A stronger, less injury-prone lower back;
• A sturdier centre of gravity, which improves your balance;
• Better running posture.

To strengthen your core and improve your running performance, perform the circuit that begins on page 60 at least once a week.

WEIGHT-TRAINING

Weight-training usually falls at the very bottom of a runner's to-do list. But it can be a terrific addition to a runner's fitness programme. Not only does strength-training tone muscles and joints – which can improve your speed and help prevent injury – but it also has many other benefits, including:

• An increase in your resting metabolism that continues for hours after your workout. Combined with cardiovascular workouts like running, cross-training offers a first-class regime for burning calories and accelerating weight loss.
• Increased bone density due to the loads weight-training places on your body. This provides protection against osteoporosis, which is especially important for women.
• More efficient breathing. Dozens of muscles throughout the torso and core come into play each time you inhale; working out with weights strengthens them so you can breathe more easily while running.

• A more balanced body, top to bottom and side to side. Weight-training will help keep your upper- and lower-body, as well as your bilateral (side-to-side) strength in parity.

The circuit workout that starts on page 63 features 8 exercises that will comprise a full-body strength training programme.

How much weight should you lift? Enough that you can do 8 to 12 reps *while maintaining proper form.* If you can't lift the weight at least 8 times without struggling, get a lighter weight; if you can zoom through 15 reps, get one that's heavier.

POOL RUNNING

Why try this exercise? Because it just may be the best cross-training for runners, and it is a completely non-impact activity, since you don't touch the bottom of the pool. We offer a range of pool-running workouts beginning on page 68.

STAIR CLIMBING

Ever want a real break from the roads and trails? Find a high-rise with a stairwell at least 10 flights tall and lace up your shoes for a stair climbing workout. Contrary to what you might think, running stairs offers less impact on your joints than hill running, while helping to improve your hill work once you return to regular running. Stair climbing is a great low-impact workout that offers a change of pace while building cardio-vascular strength. Boost your fitness with the sample stair climbing workout on page 70.

Strength-training can improve your running.

Core Conditioning

Make this core training circuit part of your routine and you'll reap benefits straightaway. All you need is an exercise mat and a stopwatch. Set the watch alarm to sound every 30 seconds and then start the first exercise. Do as many repetitions as you can until the alarm sounds, and then switch to the next exercise. If you become fatigued before the 30 seconds is up, rest until it's time to begin the next exercise. Start with 6 minutes total, and gradually work your way up to 12 minutes as your core strength improves.

CROSSOVER CRUNCH

TARGET: Obliques

❶ Lie on your back with your knees bent and feet flat on the floor.

❷ With your hands behind your head, raise your shoulders off the floor and twist towards your left knee. Lower to the starting position and repeat, this time twisting to your right knee.

INS AND OUTS

TARGET: Upper and lower abs

1 Lie on your back, hands at your sides or under your buttocks. Lift your legs about 15 cm (6 inches) off the floor.

2 Bend your legs and pull them in towards your chest.

3 Extend your legs straight up, and lift your buttocks slightly off the floor.

4 Bend your legs and pull them towards your chest again.

STRAIGHT LEG FLUTTER KICK
TARGET: Lower abs

Lie on your back with your hands by your sides, and both feet 15 cm (6 inches) off the floor. Keeping your legs straight, kick your feet in a flutter-kick motion.

V-CRUNCH
TARGET: Upper arms and lower abs

Lie flat on your back with your legs straight, heels just off the ground, and arms extended above your head. Do not arch your lower back. Lift your legs while simultaneously raising your chest and reaching for your toes (your body makes a V shape). Return to starting position.

Weight-Training

To perform this circuit, do 1 set of 8 to 12 repetitions of each exercise, in the order presented, 1 to 3 times every week. The slower you perform each rep, the longer your body is under load, and the more you will work out the target muscles. Aim for a final rep in a given set that is just about all you can manage without losing form. Gradually work up to 2, and then 3, sets of each exercise.

DUMBBELL SQUAT

TARGET: Thighs and buttocks

1 Stand up straight with your feet shoulder width apart. Hold the dumbbells at your sides.

2 Squat, keeping your chest up and your back straight. At the bottom of the squat, your thighs should be parallel to the ground. Slowly return to standing position.

LEG CURL
TARGET: Hamstrings

1 On a leg-curl machine, lie face-down on the bench, and hook the heels of your feet under the weight.

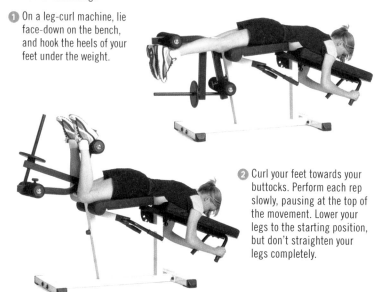

2 Curl your feet towards your buttocks. Perform each rep slowly, pausing at the top of the movement. Lower your legs to the starting position, but don't straighten your legs completely.

SUPINE DUMBBELL PRESS
TARGET: Chest

1 Lie face-up on the floor with your knees up, or on a bench with your feet flat on the floor. Hold the dumbells at about chest level with your upper arms parallel to the floor.

2 Press the dumbbells up, straightening your arms. At the top of the movement, bring the dumbbells together and squeeze. Do not arch your back, and don't let your upper arms go below chest level.

POWER CLEAN
TARGET: Full body

1 With a barbell on the floor and your feet and arms shoulder-width apart, squat, grasping the bar. Keep your head and back straight.

2 Stand up rapidly, and pull the bar towards your chest with your arms.

3 Rest the weight across your upper chest and then lower the weight with control.

SUPINE DUMBBELL TRICEP EXTENSION

TARGET: Triceps

❶ Lie on a weight bench, your feet flat on the floor. Hold a dumbbell in each hand, arms straight up, so the dumbbells are over your shoulders.

❷ Lower the dumbbells to either side of your head by bending your elbows until your forearms are parallel with the floor, then return to the starting position.

LYING KNEE HIGH CRUNCH

TARGET: Upper and lower abs

❶ Lie on the floor with your feet on a bench or chair. Place your hands at the sides of your head, your elbows pointing out.

❷ Slowly curl your chin towards your chest until your shoulder blades are off the floor. Hold for 2 seconds, then slowly lower yourself.

ONE ARM DUMBBELL ROW
TARGET: Back

① With a dumbbell in your right hand and your left knee on the bench, lean forwards so your back is parallel with the floor. Brace yourself with your left hand, allow your right arm to hang straight down.

② Pull the dumbbell slowly towards your lower abdomen, then return to the starting position.

STANDING SIDE DUMBBELL LATERAL RAISE
TARGET: Shoulders

① Stand with arms at your side, holding a dumbbell in each hand, palms facing in.

② Raise the dumbbells slowly outwards to shoulder height, then lower to the starting position. Keep your arms straight, and don't lean forwards.

Pool Running

Water is great for training, offering high resistance and low impact.

Pool running is as simple as land running; you just get into the water and start running. If you know how to run, you know how to pool run. You can enjoy the many benefits of running in water with the following workouts – or make up your own.

First, a few words about *why* you should include water running in your fitness programme. For starters, it provides an extremely effective workout. Other perks of pool running include:

- Overall conditioning of many of the body's major muscle groups – legs, arms, shoulders and core – because you're working against the resistance of the water.
- Excellent aerobic conditioning.
- Flexible resistance because water is isokinetic – the harder you push against it, the more resistance it offers you.

- No impact at all, making pool running perfect for maintaining fitness while recovering from injury. In fact, most runners experience no loss of fitness when pool running exclusively for up to 6 weeks.
- Improved range of motion, especially when you follow the proper techniques.
- Provides improved joint strength and flexibility, even for those suffering from arthritis and other joint problems – since it increases joint strength and flexibility – and for pregnant women; the

buoyant, cooling effect of the water makes for easier, lower-impact running in the second and third trimesters.

For this workout – which is simply running in water – all you need is access to a pool and a flotation belt or vest specially designed for water running.

How do you run in a pool? As any swimmer will tell you, it's all about technique. Follow these simple guidelines:

- Stay in the deep end of the pool – your toes should not touch the bottom – and of course keep your head out of the water.
- Sweep your legs from the hips to the toes with a pendulum-like motion; avoid bending your knees.
- Bend your toes downwards (think of a ballet dancer's curved foot).
- Straighten your arms and swing them alongside your body with the same motion as your legs.
- Keep your leg sweep relatively short – approximately 60 degrees of arc (imagine a clock on the bottom of the pool; keep your leg sweep between 5 and 7 o'clock).
- Align your head, chest and hips, and stay vertical; if you're moving around the pool, you're probably leaning forward. Listen to Mum's advice, and stand up straight.

WORKOUTS

Simulate your running workouts in the water, working with your expected times instead of distance. Remember that the water's density will mean your running cadence will be slower, so pay attention to your perceived level of exertion. Here are a few sample workouts:

- To simulate an interval in which you would run 800-metre repeats might mean running hard for 2½ minutes, with 30 seconds active recovery, per repeat (see pages 36–39).
- Do half of your long run on land, then jump in the pool for the second half, maintaining your prior level of exertion for as long as you spent running on the road.
- Warm up for 10 minutes, then run at 5-K pace for 2 minutes, followed by 2 minutes of easy recovery. Begin with 3 of these 2-minute intervals per session, and then gradually increase the number to 10.

If you want to focus on flexibility, move your hips, knees and ankle joints through a greater-than-usual range of motion during a 30- to 40-minute pool running workout, while keeping your exertion at a moderate level.

Stair Climbing

Stair climbing provides the same aerobic workout as running – with the added benefit of delivering a terrific workout for your calves, thighs and buttocks.

Running stairs offers less impact on your joints than hill running, while offering a number of different benefits such as increased endurance. But that's only one benefit among many. Stair running once or twice a month will provide excellent training for the primary muscle groups used in running, with more time spent in the 'push-off' phase of your stride. In addition, it will improve your endurance and cardiovascular conditioning.

Proper form is essential, so keep these tips in mind:
- Take steps one at a time.
- Don't hunch over at the waist, even though your body will naturally lean forwards.
- Look straight ahead and keep your head and chest up.
- Keep your feet as flat as you can as you land on each step to work your quads and buttocks; landing on the balls of your feet can overwork the calves and strain the Achilles tendon.

STAIR WORKOUT

Run a 3-km (2-mile) warm-up outside, then head for the stairwell (10 flights of 8 to 10 steps each is optimum). As you climb, your effort should feel as hard as quarter-mile repeats done at your 5-K pace. Engage in active recovery for the same amount of time it took you to ascend, then repeat 2 to 3 times. Finish up with an easy 15 minutes of jogging for your cool-down.

PART V:
TRAINING FOR THE NEXT LEVEL

Achieve Your Goals

Running with your spouse or partner can motivate you to meet your goals.

When you first started running, your goals were simple:
Run 5 minutes, run a mile (1.5 km), complete the workout,
finish the race. As you've improved, your ambitions have
become more complex, building from simply becoming
more fit or losing 5 kilos (10 pounds) to running a marathon. Transforming those aspirations into concrete goals
that you can measure – and reach – will supercharge your
workouts and focus your mental energies.

The most compelling reason
to set running goals is that the
habit can spread into other areas
of your life. Find success in
your running life and, chances
are, you'll see improvement in
your work and home lives, too.
Here are seven guidelines that
will help you to transform your
daydreams into realities:

1. Set specific goals that you can
   measure. For instance, 'run more
   this month', is not a measurable
   goal; 'run 45 minutes 4 times a
   week this month', is.
2. Balance challenge with achiev-
   ability. Setting unrealistic goals
   (run 350 miles [565 km] this
   month) will only build you up
   for failure and discouragement.

Make your goals challenging enough that you can reach them – if you put in the work.

3. Know that the fitter you are, the smaller the improvement you'll see for a given amount of time. When you're a beginner, you improve in leaps and bounds. The longer you run and the fitter you become, you'll find that improvements come in smaller increments; don't let that discourage you.

4. Work out a realistic time frame for achieving your goals – neither too long nor too short. If you've just started running, it would be unrealistic to expect to run a marathon in 6 weeks.

5. Write your goals down so that you won't forget or ignore them. Keep a journal of your goals and refer to it often to keep them at the top of your mind.

6. Craft success in terms of performance, not outcome (for example, decreasing your 5-K time by 10 seconds, rather than finishing first). If you focus on competing against your old self, you're more likely to enjoy real success.

7. Review your goals periodically to make sure they still make sense for you. As you near your goals, set new ones.

GOALS 101

Everyone has set an outrageous New Year's resolution only to break it shortly thereafter. Don't fall into this trap. Follow the steps below and you are bound to succeed.

The goal must be yours
You'll never put your heart into training for a marathon if you're doing it for someone other than yourself. The vision must be yours.

Be committed If you find yourself setting and then discarding goals, you must ask yourself whether they truly meant something to you to begin with.

Be confident Believing that you can reach your goals is the first step towards achieving them.

Break each goal into smaller goals Each goal you set should (1) be part of a larger goal; and (2) be able to be broken down into smaller goals. In other words, each smaller goal is a discrete step in a ladder of increasingly challenging goals or targets.

HEAD TO CAMP

You may hear the words 'running camp' and think 'kids', but in fact, many running camps are designed for families or even exclusively for adults. A week or just a few days at a camp can do wonders for your running – mentally and physically, providing you with:

• Increased motivation for months to follow.
• A solid programme for reaching your running goal.
• Coaching and critique of your running form.
• Lots of running information to boost your understanding of the sport.
• Connections with similarly motivated runners who will quite likely become lifelong friends.

Most running camps fall into one of two types: Competitive camps that focus on honing your fitness to a fine edge for better competition, and lifestyle camps that build on your love of running as a pleasurable end in and of itself. More than faster times, most lifestyle campers just want to run injury-free.

Competitive camps tend to have a strong focus on distance and speed work, featuring challenging workouts designed to push your upper speed limit. Seminars focus on training and motivation. Lifestyle camps, on the other hand, tend to feature the social aspects of running with group runs and hikes, seminars about health and fitness, and lots of running and training

A DAY AT RUNNING CAMP

Every camp is different, but most lifestyle camps follow a basic schedule that looks something like this:

7:00 to 8:00 A.M.	Morning run
8:00 to 9:30 A.M.	Breakfast
10:00 to noon	Clinics on training, motivation, nutrition, etc.
12:00 to 1:00 P.M.	Lunch
1:00 to 3:00 P.M.	Outdoor activities such as hiking or swimming
3:00 to 5:00 P.M.	Shopping, sightseeing, T-shirt swapping or cross-training clinics
6:00 to 7:00 P.M.	Dinner

All followed by lots of running talk

Lifestyle running camps focus more on the social aspects of running.

chats over meals and breaks. This sort of camp would be better suited for the casual runner.

If you're considering signing up, here are some questions to ask camp staff before you make your choice:

- What is the average age of participants in the camp?
- What is the percentage of participants in your age group?
- What kind of running improvement should I expect?

- Do you offer individualized training programmes? If so, is there an additional cost?
- Can I get free follow-up advice by e-mail?
- What types of running clinics are offered?
- Is running form evaluated on an individual basis?
- What other fun/enrichment activities are offered?
- What percentage of the campers are returnees?

Review Your Log

You've been keeping a training log for months, but now is the perfect time to take your journal to a new level. See it for what it offers, and capitalize on those benefits in new ways.

SEE HOW FAR YOU'VE COME

Reading over your old journal entries will instantly take you back to the runner you were, and will reward you with a sense of how far you've come. Utilize this motivating moment whenever you need it, especially when you feel like you're stalled at a training plateau.

SEE PATTERNS

The notes you place in your training log about your aches, pains, sprains and full-blown injuries will probably follow a pattern, for example, a weak right ankle or tight hamstrings that never seem to really loosen. Let these revelations guide your cross-training activities; with time and patience, your attention to these weak links will bring them up to par, your performance will benefit, and perhaps you can even prevent recurrent injuries from returning.

NOTE THE DETAILS

Recording your interval split times may seem nitpicky at first, but over time you will become increasingly glad of the habit you've maintained. The same logic applies to the basic data supplied by your heart-rate monitor. The bottom line: As important as it is to listen to your body's signals, it's just as important to log the basic performance data to benchmark your progress over time. View your time entries as proof positive that you've graduated from beginning to intermediate running, and you won't begrudge the extra effort.

Reviewing your log can help you see how far you've come.

BE INSPIRED

It's crucial to record those moments of inspiration, like your first race, when you see a clear path between the runner you are today and the runner you know you can become – as fleeting as they may be. Hold onto them through your log, and like the entries about your weak links, let these moments of clarity guide your long term goal-setting over the next 6 months to a year.

GUARD AGAINST OVERTRAINING

Getting yourself into peak condition can be a tricky proposition. The drive and dedication you exhibit on your way to achieving your running goals takes you perilously close to burnout, since you have to stress your body to near its limit, time and again. Do you go over the edge? Sure, every runner does. What you do when you're on the precipice makes all the difference to your training. Push too little, and you stop progressing; push too hard, and you'll bring on injury. Pushing at the right level is what it's all about. Some of the physical symptoms of overtraining include tired legs, sleeplessness, a sudden drop in weight, and occasional emotional irritability.

Whether you notice these symptoms one at a time or all at once, you might naturally wish to chalk them up to something other than running. After all, you are a motivated runner, and don't you often feel best once you do that big workout on your schedule? Most times, the answer is yes. But there could be other stresses in your life that may be combining to prevent you from feeling your best: like poor sleep, relationship problems, holidays or illnesses. Not all training plateaus can be attributed to overtraining.

None of these is unusual, and each can be the precursor to an off-day or -week. The trick is acknowledging their role, and building enough rest into your schedule to balance them.

Balance is what we all strive for. Use your training log to chart your body's aches, pains and twinges; keep stress from your life outside of running to a minimum – make sure you don't let it trip you up. And always remember that rest is not something you earn so much as deserve, so resist the temptation to skip your rest days or weeks, the overall benefits to you and your running are well worth it. Enjoy them as an essential part of your training.

The 5-K Plan

This 5-K training plan features three components: intervals run at your 5-K pace (pace intervals); intervals run slightly faster than your 5-K pace (speed intervals); and a weekly hill–training session, in addition to your usual distance.

Follow this 6-week programme through to completion, and – in addition to improvements in your 5-K race times – you should also experience improvement in your leg and glute strength, your aerobic capacity and stride length, and your ankle *flexion* (your ankle's ability to spring forwards off the ground).

YOUR FIRST RACE?

Whether you've been running for 8 months or 8 years, the 5-K will probably be the first race distance you ever run. And there are good reasons for that: the 5-K (which converts to 3.1 miles) is perhaps the most common race distance in the world, which means a runner can usually find a race close to home. This is also a great race for friends to run together. And because it is such a short distance, runners find it easy to see improvements in their race times.

This programme is designed for runners who have completed at least one 5-K 'just to finish', and who want to improve their time.

TRAINING TRUTHS

To run and race successfully, you must pay close attention to these 4 training universals:

Rest On these days, cross-train lightly with a walk, cycle or swim, but take it easy, and do not run. Your body needs a chance to recover before the next big run.

Easy runs These should be run at a comfortable pace during which you can hold a conversation, or 65 to 75 percent of your MHR (see *Heart-Rate Training*, page 29).

Long Runs These are endurance building workouts, run at distances greater than 5-K. These should also be run at a conversational pace, or 65 to 75 percent of your MHR.

Speed runs Shorter intervals (less than 5-K) at or slightly faster than your goal race pace, at efforts you would call hard to almost flat-out (87 to 95 percent of your MHR). The results are worth it: increased leg speed, cardiovascular and stride efficiency and experience

THE 5-K RACE PLAN – BEGINNER

WEEK	M	T	W	T	F	S	S	TOTAL
1	Rest	6x400m PI	3.2–8.1 km, (2–5 miles) easy	Hills, 5–8 min	Rest	3.2–8.1 km, (2–5 miles) easy	6.4–9.6 km, (4–6 miles) easy	27.3–40.2 km (17–25 miles)
2	Rest	2x800m PI, 2x400m PI, 2x200m PI	3.2–8.1 km, (2–5 miles) easy	Hills, 5–8 min	Rest	3.2–8.1 km, (2–5 miles) easy	6.4–9.6 km, (4–6 miles) easy	27.3–40.2 km (17–25 miles)
3	Rest	2x800m PI, 2x400m SI, 4x200m SI	3.2–8.1 km, (2–5 miles) easy	Hills, 6–9 min	Rest	3.2–8.1 km, (2–5 miles) easy	8.1–11.2 km, (5–7 miles) easy	30.5–40.2 km (19–25 miles)
4	Rest	2x800m PI, 1x800m SI, 2x400m SI, 2x200m SI	3.2–8.1 km, (2–5 miles) easy	Hills, 6–9 min	Rest	3.2–8.1 km, (2–5 miles) easy	8.1–12.9 km, (5–8 miles) easy	30.5–45.1 km (19–28 miles)
5	Rest	2x800m SI, 4x400m SI, 4x200m SI	3.2–8.1 km, (2–5 miles) easy	Hills, 7–10 min	Rest	3.2–8.1 km, (2–5 miles) easy	9.6–14.5 km, (6–9 miles) easy	33.8–48.3 km (21–30 miles)
6 Taper	Rest	4x400m SI, 4x200m SI	3.2–8.1 km, (2–5 miles) easy	Rest	3x200m SI, 3x150m SI, 6x100m SI	Rest	5-K Race	

Pace Intervals (PI) If your 5-K goal is a 10:00 pace (31:02 finishing time), run pace intervals at 1:15 (200m/218.7yd), 2:30 (400m/0.25 mile), 5:00 (800m/0.5 mile). For 9:00 goal pace (27:56), it's 1:07 (200m/218.7yd), 2:15 (400m/0.25 mile), 4:30 (800m/0.5 mile). For 8:00 minute goal pace (24:50), it's 1:00 (200m/218.7yd), 2:00 (400m/0.25 mile), 4:00 (800m/0.5 mile). For 7:00 goal pace (21:44), it's 0:53 (200m/218.7yd), 1:45 (400m/0.25 mile), 3:30 (800m/0.5 mile).

Speed Intervals (SI) For 10:00 pace, run 1:11 (200m/218.7yd), 2:22 (400m/0.25 mile), 4:44 (800m/0.5 mile). For 9:00 pace, it's 1:04 (200m/218.7yd), 2:08 (400m/0.25 mile), 4:15 (800m/0.5 mile). For 8:00 pace, it's 0:56 (200 m/218.7yd), 1:53 (400m/0.25 mile), 3:45 (800m/0.5 mile). For 7:00 pace, it's 0:49 (200m/218.7yd), 1:38 (400m/0.25 mile), 3:15 (800m/0.5 mile).

Recovery Time For pace intervals, slowly jog half the distance of the repetition (i.e., 200m/218.7yd jog after 400m repetitions). For speed intervals, jog equal distance (i.e., 400m/0.25 mile jog after 400m/0.25 mile repetitions).

Hills and Easy Runs For 9:00 pace, use the lower number; 7:00 runners move towards the higher.

Interval and Hill Days Jog 3.2 km (2 miles), then run 4x100m/109yd strides to get primed before the workout. Jog 3.2 km (2 miles) to cool down after, then stretch.

tolerating the rigours of racing at or above your lactate threshold (see page 80).

ON RACE DAY

Rein yourself in for the first third of the race; you may be tempted to go out fast because your training will leave you feeling strong, but don't. Instead, keep your heart rate at 75 to 80 percent of your MHR. During the second third of the race, accelerate to a comfortably hard pace, around 85 percent of your MHR. When you hit the homestretch, the last third of the race, you can reach deep for extra speed. In fact, you should be running in the 'discomfort zone' – at or above your lactate threshold. Finally, for the last 400 metres (¼ mile), reach for your reserve power to finish strong.

The 10-K plan

Like a 5-K race, the 10-K can serve you in a variety of ways: as a goal in itself, or as part of a training programme for a 5-K, half-marathon or full marathon down the line. Without a doubt, its intermediate length draws on the three hallmark components of distance running – strength, stamina and speed – making it a classic race format. Our 6-week plan will prepare you not only to finish, but to achieve your personal record goal.

ABOUT THE PLAN

The 10-K (6.2-mile) plan focuses on adding mileage to build up your endurance for race day, and adds tempo runs to make you more efficient while running near or at your lactate threshold, which is the speed you are able to run before lactic acid begins to accumulate in the blood. As with the 5-K plan, you'll also incorporate some interval and hill training for strength and speed.

TRAINING TRUTHS

Your body needs a balanced schedule of running and rest to keep it performing at peak level.

Rest No running at all – not even light cross-training.

Easy runs These should be run at a comfortable pace, one during which you can talk (65 to 75 percent of your MHR). You might be tempted to go faster, but hold yourself back.

Long runs These are primarily endurance building workouts, run at distances greater than 10-K, but at the same pace you'd run the easy runs (above). Finding a partner to run these with on a weekly basis will help keep you both motivated and enjoying the experience.

Speed work Shorter intervals at or slightly faster than your goal pace, at a hard to almost flat-out effort (about 85 to 95 percent of your MHR, see page 29). The results are increased leg speed, cardiovascular and stride efficiency and experience tolerating the rigours of racing at or above your lactate threshold.

ON RACE DAY

Either of 2 scenarios can guide you: Think of the race as 2 5-Ks; run the first at a comfortable pace and build up speed steadily for the second. Your other choice is to mentally split your 10-K into 3 with the first at a comfortable

THE 10-K RACE PLAN – BEGINNER

WEEK	M	T	W	T	F	S	S	TOTAL
1	Rest	3.2 km, (2 miles) 1 or 2x10–10, 3.2 km, (2 miles)	6.4 km (4 miles)	1x400m PI, 1x800m PI, 1x1200m PI, 1x800m PI, 1x400m PI	Rest	6.4 km (4 miles) 4x100m S	9.7–11.3 km (6–7 miles)	38.6 km (24 miles)
2	Rest	9.7 km, (6 miles) incl. 6:00 TUT	6.4 km (4 miles)	1x1200m PI, 2x800m PI, 4x200m PI, 4x200m SI, 4x100m S	Rest	7.2 km, (4.5 miles) 5x100m S	11.3–12.9 km 7–8 miles	41.8 km (26 miles)
3	Rest	3.2 km, (2 miles) 2 or 3 x 10–10, 3.2 km (2 miles)	6.4 km (4 miles)	1x800m PI, 1x1200m PI, 1x800m PI, 2x400m SI, 4x200m SI	Rest	8.1 km, (5 miles) 6x100m S	11.3–12.9 km (7–8 miles)	44.3 km (27.5 miles)
4	Rest	9.7–11.3 km, (6–7 miles), incl. 8:00 TUT	6.4 km (4 miles)	1x1200m SI, 1x800m SI, 2x400m SI, 2x200m SI, 4x100m S	Rest	8.1 km, (5 miles) 6x100m S	12.9–14.5 km (8–9 miles)	46.7 km (29 miles)
5	Rest	3.2 km, (2 miles), 3 or 4 x10–10, 3.2 km (2 miles)	6.4 km (4 miles)	1x800m SI, 4x400m SI, 4x200m SI, 1x800m SI, 4x100m S	Rest	9.7 km, (6 miles) 6x100m S	12.9–14.5 km (8–9 miles)	49.9 km (31 miles)
6 Taper	Rest	800m SI, 2x200m SI, 400m SI, 2x200m SI, 6x100m S	6.4 km (4 miles) 4x200m SI, 4x100m S	Rest	4.8 km (3 miles) easy, 3x100m S	Rest	10–K Race	

Pace Intervals (PI) Run at 10-K goal pace to improve efficiency and stamina, and to give you the feel of your race pace. For 10:00 pace (a 1:02:06 10-K), run 2:30 (400 meters/0.25 mile), 5:00 (800m/0.5 mile), 7:30 (1200m/0.75 mile). For 9:00 pace (55:53), run 2:15 (400m/0.25 mile), 4:30 (800m/0.5 mile), 6:45 (1200m/0.75). For 8:00 pace (49:40), 2:00 (400m/0.25 mile), 4:00 (800m/0.5 mile), 6:00 (1200m/0.75 mile). With pace and speed intervals (below), jog half the interval distance to recover.

Speed Intervals (SI) Run these at 30 seconds-per-mile faster than goal pace. For 10:00 pace, run 2:22 (400m/0.25 mile), 4:44 (800m/0.5 mile), 7:06 (1200m/0.75 mile). For 9:00 pace, 2:08 (400m), 4:16 (800m/0.5 mile), 6:24 (1200m/0.75 mile). For 8:00 pace, 1:53 (400m/0.25 mile), 3:45 (800m/0.5 mile), 5:38 (1200m/0.75 mile). 10–10s: 10-minute tempo repeats at 30 seconds per mile slower than 10-K goal pace; 3- to 5-minute slow jog after each.

Total Uphill Time (TUT) The total number of minutes you spend running up inclines at a 10-K effort (not pace), be they repeats up the same hill, or total uphill time over a hilly loop.

Strides (S): Over 100 metres, gradually accelerate to about 90 percent of all-out, hold it there for 5 seconds, then smoothly decelerate. Walk to full recovery after each.

pace, the second at tempo pace and the third at a hard pace. Breaking the race down into smaller sections allows you to focus on more manageable goals which, in turn, will give you the boost of mental energy you will need to finish strong.

The Half-Marathon Plan

If you've tried a 5-K or 10-K, the half-marathon may be the next big distance you want to strive for. As a stamina booster and body strengthener, you could do a lot worse; gearing up for a half-marathon will make your future 5- and 10-K races more competitive on many levels. The distance is a challenge, certainly, but recovering from the race will take you only a week, in contrast to the month off you generally need after draining your tank with a full marathon.

ABOUT THE PLANS

Because of the longer training time, we're offering two half-marathon plans – one for those who have never ran a half-marathon before, and one for intermediate runners with a few more races under their belts.

TRAINING TRUTHS

To balance the pounding your legs will take during the weeks leading up to any race you must be sure to balance your training.

Rest No running at all – not even light cross-training.

Easy runs These should be run at a comfortable pace for an on-the-run chat. You might be tempted to go faster, but hold yourself back.

Long runs These are primarily endurance builders, at distances greater than 10-K (6.2 miles). Find-ing a partner to run these with on a weekly basis will help keep you both motivated.

Speed work Shorter intervals at or slightly faster than your goal race pace, at efforts you would call

Be sure to stop for a drink when you need one.

THE HALF-MARATHON RACE PLAN – BEGINNER

WEEK	M	T	W	T	F	S	S	TOTAL
1	Rest	2 miles (3.2 km) 5–7x1:00 AI, 2 miles	Rest	4 miles (6.4 km) + 4 GP	Rest	3–4 miles (4.8–6.4 km)	6–7 miles (9.7–11.3 km)	19–21 miles (30.6–33.8 km)
2	Rest	2 miles (3.2 km), 5–7x1:00 AI, 2 miles	Rest	4 miles (6.4 km) + 4 GP	Rest	3–4 miles (4.8–6.4 km)	6–7 miles (9.7–11.3 km)	19–21 miles (30.6–33.8 km)
3	Rest	2 miles (3.2 km), 2x[1:00, 1:30, 2:00] AI, 2 miles	Rest	4 miles (6.4 km), incl. 4x1:00 AI + 5–6 GP	Rest	5-K race	4–5 miles (4.6–8.1 km)	22–24 miles (35.4–38.6 km)
4	Rest	3 miles (4.8 km), 3x[2:00, 2:30] AI, 2 miles (3.2 km)	Rest	5–6 miles (8.1–9.7 km), incl. 4x1:30 AI + 6 GP	Rest	3–4 miles (4.8–6.4 km)	7–8 miles (11.3–12.9 km)	24–26 miles (38.6–41.8 km)
5	Rest	3 miles (4.8 km), 3x[2:00, 2:30] AI, 2 miles (3.2 km)	Rest	5–6 miles (8.1–9.7), incl. 4x1:30 AI + 6 GP	Rest	3–4 miles (4.8–6.4 km)	7–8 miles (11.3–12.9 km)	24–26 miles (38.6–41.8 km)
6	Rest	3 miles (4.8 km), 2x2:00 AI, 2x2:30 AI, 1x3:00 AI+6 GP, 2 miles (3.2 km) 6x100m S	Rest	5–6 miles (8.1–9.7 km) + 4 GP	Rest	10-K race	4 miles (6.4 km)	27–30 miles (43.5–48.3 km)
7	Rest	3 miles (4.8 km), 2x[2:00. 3:00, 4:00] AI, 2 miles (3.2 km)	Rest	6 miles (9.7 km), incl. 4x2:00 AI + 6 GP	Rest	5–6 miles (8.1–9.7 km)	9–10 miles (14.5–16.1 km)	32–34 miles (51.5–54.7 km)
8	Rest	3 miles (4.8 km), 2x[2:00. 3:00, 4:00] AI, 2 miles	Rest	6 miles (9.7 km), incl. 4x2:00 AI + 6 GP	Rest	5–6 miles (8.1–9.7 km)	9–10 miles (14.5–16.1 km)	32–34 miles (54.7–57.9 km)
9 Taper	Rest	2 miles (3.2 km), 4x1:00 AI	Rest	2 miles (3.2 km) easy, 4 x GP	Rest	2 miles (3.2 km)	Half–marathon race	

Aerobic Intervals (AI) You increase your pace slightly for a specific length of time (one to several minutes, per the plan), slow to a jog while your breathing recovers, then return to your regular pace.

Gentle Pick-ups (GP) Less intense than strides, GPs involve gradually accelerating on a flat 100m (109-yds) stretch until you're breathing hard, holding it there for 10–20m (10.9 to 21.8 yds), then slowly ramping it back down. Walk to a full recovery before starting your next GP. Work these into the end of your workouts before your cool-down.

hard to almost flat-out. The results are worth it: increased leg speed, cardiovascular strength and stride efficiency, and experience tolerating the rigours of racing that come along with running at or above your lactate threshold (see page 32).

THE BEGINNER PLAN

Building up your distance and endurance are the goals of this programme. By the end of this plan, you will not only be ready to race, but you will also have a tonne of 2-hour, 10-mile (16.1 km) plus

Take time to cool down and stretch after a race.

keep going. Your pre-race taper plus the energy and excitement of race day will get you through, all the way to the finish line.

THE INTERMEDIATE PLAN

Intermediate runners have enough experience and strength to support some faster running – within the training context of increased distance and a weekly long run. That means tempo-pace training at the end of longer runs is a key component of this plan. Expect some mile intervals, too, at faster-than-race pace, with good recovery afterwards – that means getting your heart rate down to around 120 beats per minute with a ¼ mile (400 metre) jog.

ON RACE DAY

Keep your warm-up fairly light – an 800-metre (½ mile) jog and a few fast strides – to keep yourself as fresh as possible for the race. Treat the first 10 miles (16.1 km) of the race like a long-distance run, keeping your heart rate at around 75 percent of your MHR, working up to your goal pace over the first mile, then run the last 3 miles like a 5-K race, at, but not above your lactate threshold. Bypass other runners when you can, and you'll finish feeling good.

training runs behind you – rites of passage and worthy accomplishments in their own right.

ON RACE DAY

Keep it slow and comfortable to start, and work your way into a controlled rhythm as the race continues. Stop at every aid station – eat, drink, stretch if you need to, even rest for up to 30 seconds – and then

THE HALF-MARATHON RACE PLAN – INTERMEDIATES

WEEK	M	T	W	T	F	S	S	TOTAL
1	Rest	1x1200 PI (400), 2x800 CI (200), 4x200 SI (200)	3–4 miles (4.8–6.4 km), or rest	2x2 miles (3.2 km) PI (800) + 4x100 S	Rest	4 miles (6.4 km) + 4x100 S	8–9 miles (12.9–14.5 km)	26–30 miles (41.8–48.3 km)
2	Rest	1x1200 PI (400), 2x800 CI (200), 4x200 SI (200)	3–4 miles (4.8–6.4 km), or rest	2x2 miles (3.2 km) PI (800) + 4x100S	Rest	4 miles (6.4 km) + 4x100 S	8–9 miles (12.9–14.5 km) incl. 4:00 TUT	26–30 miles (41.8–48.3 km)
3	Rest	2x[1200 CI (600), 800 CI (400), 400 SI (200)]	2 miles (3.2 km)	3 miles (4.8 km) + 4x100 S	Rest	5-K race	6 miles (9.7 km)	24 miles (38.6 km)
4	Rest	2x1–mile, CI (800), 6x200 SI (200)	3–4 miles (4.8–6.4 km), or rest	4 miles (6.4 km) PI (800), 1 mile CI + 6x100 S	Rest	5 miles (8.1 km) + 6x100 S	10 miles (16.1 km), incl. 6:00 TUT	28–32 miles (45.1–51.5 km)
5	Rest	2x1–mile CI (800), 6x200 SI (200)	3–4 miles (4.8–6.4 km), or rest	4 miles (6.4 km) PI (800), 1 mile CI + 6x100 S	Rest	5 miles (8.1 km) + 6x100 S	11 miles (17.7 km)	28–32 miles (45.1–51.5 km)
6	Rest	2x[800 SI (400), 400 SI (200), 200 SI (200), 1200 PI)]	3–4 miles (4.8–6.4 km), or rest	4 miles (6.4 km) (incl. 6x1:00 SI) + 4x100 S	Rest	10-K race	8 miles (12.9 km)	30 miles (48.3 km)
7	Rest	2x1200 CI (600), 4x400 SI (200), 4x200 SI (100)	3–4 miles (4.8–6.4 km), or rest	4 miles (6.4 km) PI (800), 1x800 CI (400), 2 miles PI	Rest	6 miles (9.7 km) + 6x100 S	11–12 miles (17.7–19.3 km), incl. 8:00 TUT	32–36 miles (51.5–57.9 km)
8	Rest	2x1200 CI (600), 4x400 SI (200), 4x200 SI (100)	3–4 miles (4.8–6.4 km), or rest	4 miles (6.4 km) PI (800), 1x800 CI (400), 2 miles PI	Rest	6 miles (9.7 km) + 6x100 S	6 miles (9.7 km)	32–36 miles (51.5–57.9 km)
9 Taper	Rest	4x400 CI (200), 2x200 SI (100)	2 miles (3.2 km), + 4x100 S	2x400 CI (200), 1x200 SI	Rest	3 miles (4.8 km) easy	Half-marathon race	

Pace Intervals (PI) Set distances (0.75 mile/1200m, for example, or 3 miles/4.8 km) at your goal half-marathon pace to build endurance and develop pace judgement.

Cruise Intervals (CI) Run at 10-K race pace to promote stamina and the ability to run strong when tired. For 10:00-mile half-marathon pace (2:11:06), run 7:07 (0.75 mile/1200m), 4:45 (0.5 mile/800m); for 9:00 pace (1:57:59), run 6:24 (0.75 mile/1200m), 4:16 (0.5 mile/800m); for 8:00 pace (1:44:52), run 5:42 (0.75 mile/1,200m), 3:48 (0.5 mile/800m).

Speed Intervals (SI) Run at 5-K race pace to promote relaxed speed and a sense of comfort with your considerably slower half-marathon pace. For 10:00 pace, run 4:30 (0.5 mile/800m), 2:15 (0.25 mile/400m), 1:07 (218.7 yd/200m); for 9:00 pace, run 4:04 (0.5 mile/800m), 2:02 (0.25 mile/400m), 1:01 (200m/218.7 yds); for 8:00 pace, run 3:37 (0.5 mile/800m), 1:48 (0.25 mile/400m), 0:54 (218.7 yd/200m).

Strides (S) Over 109 yd/100m, gradually accelerate to 90 percent of all-out, hold it for 5 seconds, then decelerate. Walk to full recovery after each.

Total Uphill Time (TUT) The total number of minutes you spend running up inclines at a 10-K effort (not pace), be they repeats up the same hill or total uphill time over a hilly loop.

The Marathon Plan

Like a mountain daring you to climb it, the marathon looms ahead of you. To attempt this requires commitment, and completing it requires training. We've got two plans to get you over the finish line in fine form. As with the half-marathon, a beginner's plan will aid those running their first marathon, while the intermediate plan will help more experienced runners take their performance to the next level.

TRAINING TRUTHS

If you are training for a marathon, you have probably been running for a while, but following these training truths is still important:

Rest No running, no walking, no nothing.

Repeat You'll notice that the plans repeat certain training weeks. This is so that you can make changes to your pace and recovery based on your experience the first time around. Learn, then master.

Go soft Wherever possible, do your training on grass or another yielding surface to give your legs a rest from the pounding that high mileage on pavement will deliver.

Hydrate wisely Try out sports beverages during training and stick to your favourite(s) on race day so your stomach stays happy.

Become race fit Each plan features two races – a 5-K and a 10-K – to tune you up for the big one. You'll run faster in them than you can probably push yourself in training, to the benefit of your aerobic capacity and ability to run at or above your lactate threshold.

THE BEGINNER PLAN

Gradually increasing your mileage week to week, especially through your weekend long run, defines the trajectory of your training plan. Hills and some speed work will also figure into the mix, but expect to see your weekly distance climb from 15 miles (24.1 km) to almost 40 miles (64.6 km) before your pre-race taper.

ON RACE DAY

Keep your pace slow for the first half of the marathon – sightsee, chat with other runners and walk through the aid station. Build your speed slowly in the second half of the race. Hydrate, rest a bit if you need to, and then resume running slowly each time as you work your way through the race.

THE MARATHON RACE PLAN – BEGINNERS

WEEK	M	T	W	T	F	S	S	TOTAL
1	Rest	4 miles (6.4 km), incl. 4:00 TUT	Rest	1-hour run	Rest	4 miles (6.4 km)	6 miles (9.7 km)	15-16 miles (24.1–25.7 km)
2	Rest	4 miles (6.4 km), incl. 4:00 TUT	Rest	1-hour run	Rest	4 miles (6.4 km)	7 miles (11.3 km)	15-16 miles (24.1–25.7 km)
3	Rest	4 miles (6.4 km), incl. 5:00 TUT	Rest	6 miles (9.7 km)	Rest	Rest	8 miles (12.9 km)	18-19 miles (28.9–30.6 km)
4	Rest	4 miles (6.4 km), incl. 5:00 TUT	Rest	6 miles (9.7 km)	Rest	Rest	9 miles (14.5 km)	18–19 miles (28.9–30.6 km)
5	Rest	4 miles (6.4 km), incl. 3x2:00 AI	Rest	4 miles (6.4 km)	Rest	5-K race	6–8 miles (9.7–12.9 km)	19–21 miles (30.6–33.8 km)
6	Rest	5 miles (8.1 km), incl. 6:00 TUT	Rest	7 miles (11.3 km)	Rest	Rest	10 miles (16.1 km)	22–24 miles (35.4–38.6 km)
7	Rest	5 miles (8.1 km), incl. 6:00 TUT	Rest	7 miles (11.3 km)	Rest	Rest	12 miles (19.3 km)	22–24 miles (35.4–38.6 km)
8	Rest	5 miles (8.1 km), incl. 7:00 TUT	Rest	8 miles (12.9 km)	Rest	Rest	12 miles (19.3 km)	25–27 miles (40.2–43.5 km)
9	Rest	5 miles (8.1 km), incl. 6:00 TUT	Rest	8 miles (12.9 km)	Rest	Rest	14 miles (22.5 km)	25–27 miles (40.2–43.5 km)
10	Rest	5 miles (8.1 km), incl. 3x3:00 AI	Rest	4 miles (6.4 km)	Rest	10-K race	5 miles (8.1 km)	24 miles (38.6 km)
11	Rest	5 miles (8.1 km), incl. 8:00 TUT	Rest	9 miles (14.5 km)	Rest	Rest	16 miles (25.7 km)	30–32 miles (48.3–51.5 km)
12	Rest	5 miles (8.1 km), incl. 8:00 TUT	Rest	9 miles (14.5 km)	Rest	Rest	18 miles (28.9 km)	30–32 miles (48.3–51.5 km)
13	Rest	5 miles (8.1 km), incl. 9:00 TUT	Rest	10 miles (16.1 km)	Rest	4 miles (6.4 km)	20 miles (32.2 km)	39 miles (62.3 km)
14	Rest	5 miles (8.1 km), incl. 9:00 TUT	Rest	10 miles (16.1 km)	Rest	4 miles (6.4 km)	10 miles (16.1 km)	29 miles (46.7 km)
15 Taper	Rest	3 miles (4.8 km), incl. 3X3:00 AI	Rest	5 miles (8.1 km)	Rest	3 miles (4.8 km), incl. 3x2:00 AI	5 miles (8.1 km)	16 miles (25.7 km)
16 Taper	Rest	3 miles (4.8 km), Incl. 3x2:00 AI	Rest	3-mile (4.8 km) jog	Rest	2-mile (3.2 km) jog	Marathon	

Aerobic Intervals (AI) You increase your pace several minutes, per the plan, slow to a jog while your breathing recovers, then return to your regular pace.

Total Uphill Time (TUT) Work the uphill sections during your run at something near a strong 10-K effort in the total time called for.

Easy Runs These should be run at a comfortable pace for an on-the-run chat. You might be tempted to go faster, but hold yourself back.

Long Runs These are primarily endurance builders, at distances greater than 10-K. Finding a partner to run these with on a weekly basis will help keep you both motivated and enjoying the experience.

Speed Work Shorter intervals at or slightly faster than your goal race pace, at efforts you would call hard to almost flat-out. The results are worth it – increased leg speed, cardiovascular and stride efficiency, and experience tolerating the rigours of racing at or above your lactate threshold.

THE MARATHON RACE PLAN – INTERMEDIATE

WEEK	M	T	W	T	F	S	S	TOTAL
1	Rest	2 miles (3.2 km) GP 2 miles T 2 miles (TK km) GP	3 miles (4.8 km) 4x100 S	1-hour run, incl. 4:00–5:00 TUT	Rest	4 miles (6.4 km)	8 miles (12.9 km)	29–33 miles (46.7–53.1 km)
2	Rest	2 miles (3.2 km) GP 2 miles T 2 miles (TK km) GP	3 miles (4.8 km) 4x100 S	1-hour run, incl. 4:00–5:00 TUT	Rest	4 miles (6.4 km)	10 miles (16.1 km)	29–33 miles (46.7–53.1 km)
3	Rest	2 miles (3.2 km) GP 4x1 mile (1.6km) T (1:00) 2 miles GP	3 miles (4.8 km) 5x100 S	70-minute run, incl. 5:00–6:00 TUT	Rest	5 miles (8.1 km)	12 miles (19.3 km)	35–39 miles (56.3–62.3 km)
4	Rest	2 miles (3.2 km) GP 4x1 mile (1.6 km) T (1:00) 2 miles GP	3 miles (4.8 km) 5x100 S	70-minute run, incl. 5:00–6:00 TUT	Rest	5 miles (8.1 km)	14 miles (22.5 km)	35–39 miles (56.3–62.3 km)
5	Rest	4x1,200 C	3 miles (4.8 km) 4x100 S	4x800 SI	Rest	5-K race	10 miles (16.1 km)	28–30 miles (45.1–48.3 km)
6	Rest	2 miles (3.2 km) GP 2x2 miles T 3 miles (4.8 km) GP	3 miles (4.8 km) 6x100 S	80-minute run, incl. 6:00–8:00 TUT	Rest	5 miles (8.1 km)	15 miles (24.1 km)	39–43 miles (62.3–69.2 km)
7	Rest	2 miles (3.2 km) GP 2x2 miles T 3 miles (4.8 km) GP	3 miles (4.8 km) 6x100 S	80-minute run, incl. 6:00–8:00 TUT	Rest	5 miles (8.1 km)	16 miles (25.7 km)	39–43 miles (62.3–69.2 km)
8	Rest	2 miles (3.2 km) GP 3x2 miles T (2:00) 3 miles (4.8 km) GP	3 miles (4.8 km) 6x100 S	4x1 mile (1.6 km)	Rest	5 miles (8.1 km)	16 miles (25.7 km)	44–47 miles (70.8–75.6 km)
9	Rest	2 miles (3.2 km) GP 3x2 miles T (2:00) 3 miles (4.8 km) GP	3 miles (4.8 km) 6x100 S	4x1 mile (1.6 km)	Rest	5 miles (8.1 km)	17 miles (27.3 km)	44–47 miles (70.8–75.6 km)
10	Rest	1-hour run, incl. 2x1, 200 C 2x400 SI	4 miles (6.4 km)	4x800 S 6x100 S	Rest	10-K race	6-8 miles (9.7–12.9 km)	32–34 miles (51.5–54.7 km)
11	Rest	2 miles (3.2 km) GP 4x2 miles T (2:00) 3 miles (4.8 km) GP	3 miles (4.8 km) 6x100 S	90-minute run, incl. 8:00–10:00 TUT	Rest	4 miles (6.4 km)	18 miles (28.9 km)	45–51 miles (72.4–82.0 km)

THE MARATHON RACE PLAN – INTERMEDIATE (cont.)

WEEK	M	T	W	T	F	S	S	TOTAL
12	Rest	2 miles (3.2 km) GP 4x2 miles T (2:00) 3 miles (4.8 km) GP	3 miles (4.8 km) 6x100 S	90-minute run, incl. 8:00–10:00 TUT	Rest	4 miles (6.4 km)	19 miles (30.6 km)	45–51 miles (72.4–82.0 km)
13	Rest	3x1 mile (1.6) C 3x800 SI	3 miles (4.8 km) 6x100 S	75-minute run, incl 6:00–8:00 TUT	Rest	4 miles (6.4 km)	20 miles (32.2	46 miles (74.0 km)
14	Rest	3x1 mile (1.6 km) C 3x 800 SI	3 miles (4.8 km) 6x100 S	75-minute run, including 6:00–8:00 TUT	Rest	4 miles (6.4 km)	13 miles (20.9	45 miles (72.4 km)
15 taper	Rest	2 miles (3.2 km) GP 4 miles (6.4 km) T	3 miles (4.8 km) 6x100 S	1-hour run, incl. 6x400 SI	Rest	Rest	1-hour run	27–29 miles (43.5–46.7 km)
16 taper	Rest	4x400 SI	Rest	3 miles (4.8 km) 6x100 S	Rest	2-mile (3.2 km) jog	Marathon	

Marathon Goal Pace (MGP) Your per-mile goal marathon pace.

Tempo Runs (T) For 11:00 MGP (4:48:25), run 10:28 (1 mile/1.6 km); for 10:00 MGP (4:22:12), run 9:31; for 9:00 MGP (3:55:58), run 8:34. Recovery is slow jogging for the number of minutes in brackets.

Cruise Intervals (C) For 11:00 MGP, run 9:56 (1 mile/1.6 km), 7:49 (0.75 mile/1200m); for 10:00 MGP, run 9:02 and 6:47; for 9:00 MGP, run 8:07 and 6:06. Recovery is half the distance of the repetition.

Speed Intervals (SI) For 11:00 MGP, run 4:52 (0.5 mile/800m), 2:26 (0.25 mile/400m); for 10:00 MGP, run 4:17, 2:08; for 9:00 MGP, run 3:50, 1:55. Recovery is equal distance (e.g., 0.25 mile/400m jog for 0.25 mile/400m repeats).

Total Uphill Time (TUT) The total number of minutes you spend running up inclines at a 10-K effort (not pace), be they repeats up the same hill or total uphill time over a hilly loop.

Warm-up/Cool-down 15 minutes of easy running followed by 4x100m strides before each Tuesday/Thursday session, with 15 minutes of easy running afterwards.

Strides (S) over 109 yd/100m, gradually accelerate to about 90 percent of all-out, hold it there for 5 seconds, then smoothly decelerate. Walk to full recovery after each.

Running a marathon will boost your adrenaline.

THE INTERMEDIATE PLAN

The intermediate plan is designed for runners with race experience. A basic plan that can be modified to fit your needs should consist of a lot of distant running, mixed in with two tempo runs a week at half-marathon pace. Add in speed work once a week.

ON RACE DAY

Run the first 5 to 8 miles (8.1–13 km) at a pace considerably slower than your goal pace at least 10 to 15 seconds slower. Saving your energy in the beginning will allow you the burst of energy you'll need to finish the last 6 to 8 miles (9.6–13 km).

AFTER THE RACE

It's the morning after the big race and all the excitement from finishing has worn off. You are sore and tired, and racing is the furthest thing from your mind. Don't worry: The physical effects of marathoning usually subside about 3 days after you cross the finish line. That's when you'll begin to feel good and perhaps start planning for your next race. But before you head out for your first run after a 26-miler, be aware that although your legs may feel loose and ready to run, your body – mentally and chemically – still needs time to recuperate. Here are a few guidelines to follow after any marathon:

• Take a warm bath the morning after the marathon, but be sure to ice all injured areas first. You may try gentle stretching or going for a walk, but no running.

• Be sure to get as much sleep as you can in the days following the race. Your body needs rest to restore its chemical balance.

• Don't run for the first 3 to 7 days after the marathon. You may be gliding on a post-marathon high, but be aware that you should take a recovery day for every mile ran during the race (26 miles [41.8 km] equals 26 recovery days). For your recovery days you can do the reverse of the pre-marathon taper, by building up to your normal weekly distance slowly.

Injuries and Recuperation

Like death and taxes, injuries do happen from time to time. Some are obvious: You stumble over a root and twist your ankle, or push a little too hard on a hill repeat and find yourself limping home. Others are more subtle: You wake up the next morning with an odd feeling in your knee, a vague pain in your calf, or an overall feeling of fatigue.

These injuries are part of running, but how you manage them is completely within your control.

WARNING SIGNS

Listen to your body and learn to recognize warning signs. Taking the right steps early can make an annoyance remain an annoyance that will soon go away, instead of disrupting your training for weeks. **Swelling, redness and warmth** Think of swelling as your body having cordoned off the afflicted area so you won't injure it further. If you're aware of any swelling, especially in your feet or legs, skip running and take action to reduce it right away (see *RICE*, on page 92). Keep in mind that some runners may experience swollen feet and/or hands during warm weather due to dehydration. This swelling will go down if you drink enough fluids.

Loss of function You can injure yourself to the point where your stride changes to favour the injured area, without any warning signs of pain directing your attention to the area itself. How do you avoid the domino-effect injury? Pay close attention to how your stride feels under normal conditions, and check in with yourself often. Ask a running partner to take a look as well.

Pain Aches and low-grade pains that go away during a run are nothing to worry about, but if they continue during and after your run – even into the rest of the day – you've got something to keep an eye on. Don't run again until the pain has gone, or until you've sought treatment, and then proceed gingerly.

Something amiss Like loss of function, you need to be aware of your own body to detect the

Always heed the warning signs of injury.

warning signs. Call it intuition, but most runners develop a sense of when something is sub-par; smart runners take the proactive step of resting for a day to see whether the feeling goes away.

THE TREATMENTS

RICE A time-tested method, this stands for Rest, Ice, Compression and Elevation. Most of the time, rest is all you'll need, but it's a good practice to keep ice on hand in the freezer for short, 10- to 15-minute cool-downs of injured areas (a towel between the ice and your skin will provide added protection from frostbite). Compression can be accomplished by wrapping the area in a bandage, sometimes with ice underneath. Elevating the injured body part helps drain away excess fluid so that healing can happen faster.

Skip stretching The benefits you gain from stretching a healthy muscle – lengthening and strengthening it – are detrimental to a torn muscle trying to repair itself. Take a break from stretching until healing is well under way, and then ease into it very gently when your muscles are nice and warm.

Get expert advice This is no time to rely on a fellow runner's anecdotal cure. Talk to your doctor or sports therapist for the information you need to heal properly without reinjuring yourself.

Respect medications If you're dealing with inflammation, over-the-counter medications such as ibuprofen, naproxen or their anti-inflammatory cousins can be effective at reducing swelling. Nevertheless, you should use them only for short periods of time 1 to 2 weeks at most), and *never* before a run because of their effects on the stomach and sensation-dulling properties.

Return to running slowly Run only every other day at first, and skip speed work of any type for 3 weeks solid. Cut down any cross-training you might have engaged in (pool running, for example) during your recuperation period so you don't overtax your system, and don't hesitate to walk – even walk in place of running – to keep yourself from overdoing it.

By treating injuries early and staying judicious during your recovery, your episodes of injury will be short and infrequent – a few painful entries in your training log and nothing more.

RECOVER FROM THE BIG FINISH

Recovering from a big run or race is a four-stage process, starting with the first moments after you cross the finish line and extending for several weeks afterwards; this is particularly true if you've completed a marathon. Follow these easy guidelines so that recovery feels as good as you know it should – you've earned it!

STAGE 1: IMMEDIATE RECOVERY

You've crossed the finish line and the twin demons of fatigue and thirst threaten to overwhelm you. Take heart, as they'll pass quickly. The most important thing you can do is simply to keep moving. A shuffling walk is fine, and will help your heart cool down safely (whereas lying or sitting down won't). Later in the day, when you've returned to a resting state and restored your food and fluid deficit, limber up with a short, easy walk if you feel like it.

STAGE 2: MUSCLE RECOVERY

The first two days after your race is likely to acquaint you with some muscle soreness, and day 2 traditionally visits even more soreness than day one. Take these 2 days to simply rest, if you can, limiting your physical activity to low-impact easy walking, cycling or swimming if need be. Resist the twin temptations to run yourself out of the soreness (you can't) or wallow in a feeling of post-race laziness. Remember: this is a resting period, so rent a DVD and enjoy the time off – you've earned it.

STAGE 3: FULL-BODY RECOVERY

You can start running again now, but keep it slow and easy. It may be at least several days before you feel at your strongest again and that is okay; extra food and rest are essential at this stage so that you replace depleted reserves. The watchwords: don't force it, because if it feels too hard, it definitely is. The last thing you need is an injury from coming back too fast and too soon.

STAGE 4: PSYCHOLOGICAL RECOVERY

Many runners deal with post-race blues – it's natural to feel a little let-down after you've accomplished so big a goal. So don't beat yourself up if you find that you have lost the joy of running for several weeks after the big day. Believe it or not, your body is still telling you to cool your heels, so heed the signal. You don't need to give up training entirely during this period, but rather avoid anything too difficult.

Recovery is all about making sure you stay motivated for the next race, so pay attention to the 4 stages of recovery and you'll be ready for the next race quickly, rested and eager to go.

Allowing your body to rest and recover is your reward for weeks of hard training.

INDEX

Numbers in **bold** refer to pages with illustrations